Understanding Alcohol

Series Editor: Cara Acred

Volume 254

Independence Educational Publishers

First published by Independence Educational Publishers

The Studio, High Green

Great Shelford

Cambridge CB22 5EG

England

© Independence 2014

Photocopy licence

The material in this book is protected by copyright. However, the
purchaser is free to make multiple copies of particular articles for instructional
purposes for immediate use within the purchasing institution.
Making copies of the entire book is not permitted.

British Library Cataloguing in Publication Data

Understanding alcohol. -- (Issues ; 254)
1. Alcoholism. 2. Alcohol. 3. Drinking of alcoholic beverages.
I. Series II. Acred, Cara editor of compilation.
362.2'92-dc23

ISBN-13: 9781861686657

Printed in Great Britain
MWL Print Group Ltd

Contents

Introduction

Understanding Alcohol is Volume 254 in the **ISSUES** series. The aim of the series is to offer current, diverse information about important issues in our world, from a UK perspective.

ABOUT UNDERSTANDING ALCOHOL

With around nine in 100 men and four in 100 women showing signs of being dependent on alcohol, what are the long- and short-term effects of drinking? This book explores the effects of alcohol on the body and the mind, looks at drinking trends in the UK and considers the safe weekly limits for both men and women. It also looks at alcohol related accidents and the effects on hospitals, and considers whether the legal drinking age should be increased.

OUR SOURCES

Titles in the **ISSUES** series are designed to function as educational resource books, providing a balanced overview of a specific subject.

The information in our books is comprised of facts, articles and opinions from many different sources, including:

⇨ Newspaper reports and opinion pieces

⇨ Website fact sheets

⇨ Magazine and journal articles

⇨ Statistics and surveys

⇨ Government reports

⇨ Literature from special interest groups.

A NOTE ON CRITICAL EVALUATION

Because the information reprinted here is from a number of different sources, readers should bear in mind the origin of the text and whether the source is likely to have a particular bias when presenting information (or when conducting their research). It is hoped that, as you read about the many aspects of the issues explored in this book, you will critically evaluate the information presented.

It is important that you decide whether you are being presented with facts or opinions. Does the writer give a biased or unbiased report? If an opinion is being expressed, do you agree with the writer? Is there potential bias to the 'facts' or statistics behind an article?

ASSIGNMENTS

In the back of this book, you will find a selection of assignments designed to help you engage with the articles you have been reading and to explore your own opinions. Some tasks will take longer than others and there is a mixture of design, writing and research-based activities that you can complete alone or in a group.

FURTHER RESEARCH

At the end of each article we have listed its source and a website that you can visit if you would like to conduct your own research. Please remember to critically evaluate any sources that you consult and consider whether the information you are viewing is accurate and unbiased.

Useful weblinks

www.alcoholconcern.org.uk

www.alcoholpolicy.net

www.beerandpub.com

www.bupa.co.uk

www.drinkaware.co.uk

www.economicshelp.org

www.itsthedrinktalking.co.uk

www.jrf.org.uk

www.knowyourlimits.info

www.nhs.uk

www.publichealth.hscni.net

www.rcpsych.ac.uk

www.thecalmzone.net

Our favourite drug

Introduction

Alcohol is our favourite drug. Most of us use it for enjoyment, but for some of us, drinking can become a serious problem. In fact, alcohol causes much more harm than illegal drugs like heroin and cannabis. It is a tranquilliser, it is addictive, and is the cause of many hospital admissions for physical illnesses and accidents.

Problems with alcohol

Many of these problems are caused by having too much to drink at the wrong place or time. Alcohol affects your judgement, so you do things you wouldn't normally think of. It makes you less aware of risks and so more vulnerable. You are more likely to have fights, arguments, money troubles, family upsets or spur-of-the-moment casual sex. Alcohol helps to cause accidents at home, on the roads, in the water and on playing fields.

Physical health

Being very drunk can lead to severe hangovers, stomach pains (gastritis), vomiting blood, unconsciousness and even death. Drinking too much over a long period of time can cause liver disease and increases the risk of some kinds of cancer. It can reduce the risk of heart disease for men over 40 and women of menopausal age – but only if their drinking is very moderate.

Mental health

Although we tend to think of alcohol as something we use to make us feel good, heavy drinking can bring on depression. Many people who kill themselves have had drinking problems. Alcohol can stop your memory from working properly and can cause brain damage. It can even make you hear noises and voices – a very unpleasant experience which can be hard to get rid of.

Warning signs

Alcohol is addictive. Some warning signs are:

⇨ you do not feel right without a drink, or need a drink to start the day

⇨ you get very shaky, sweaty and anxious/tense a few hours after your last drink

⇨ you can drink a lot without becoming drunk

⇨ you need to drink more and more to get the same effect

⇨ you try to stop, but find you can't

⇨ you carry on drinking even though you can see it is interfering with your work, family and relationships

⇨ you get 'memory blanks' where you can't remember what happened for a period of hours or days.

Dealing with alcohol problems

If you are worried about your drinking or a friend's drinking, tell them – they need to make changes as soon as possible. It is much easier to cut back before drinking problems damage your health than it is once they are out of hand.

First steps

Keep a diary of your drinking – you may be surprised by how much you really do drink, and this can give you the motivation to cut down. It helps if you can talk your plans over with a friend or relative. Do not be ashamed to tell someone. Most real friends will be pleased to help – you may find they have been worried about you for some time.

Getting help

If you find it hard to change your drinking habits then try talking to your GP or go for advice to a local alcohol organisation. If you feel you cannot stop because you get too shaky or restless and jumpy when you try to cut down, your doctor can often help with some medication for a short time. If you still find it very difficult to change then you may need specialist help.

Changing habits

We all find it hard to change a habit, particularly one that plays such a large part in our lives. There are three steps to dealing with the problem:

⇨ Realising and accepting that there is a problem.

⇨ Getting help to break the habit.

⇨ Keeping going once you have begun to make changes.

You may find that you have been using alcohol as a way of handling stress and worries. A psychiatrist or a psychologist may be able to help you find ways of overcoming these worries that do not involve relying on drink.

Groups where you meet other people with similar problems can often be very helpful. There are self-help groups like Alcoholics Anonymous, or those run by professionals at an alcohol treatment unit.

Most people dealing with their drink problems do not need to go

Beer, Cider & Alcopops	Strength ABV	Half Pint	Pint	Bottle/Can 330 ml	Bottle/Can 500 ml	Bottle 1 litre
Ordinary strength beer, lager or cider, e.g. Draught beer, Woodpecker	3–4%	1	2	1.5	1.9	–
'Export' strength beer, lager or cider, e.g. Stella, Budweiser, Heineken, Kronenbourg, Strongbow	5%	1.25	2.5	2	2.5	–
Extra strong beer, lager or cider, e.g. Special Brew, Diamond White, Tennents Extra	8–9%	2.5	4.5	3	4.5	9
Alcopops, e.g. Bacardi Breezer, Smirnoff Ice, Reef, Archers, Hooch	5%	–	–	1.7	–	–

into hospital. Some people will need to get away from the places where they drink and the people they drink with. For them, a short time in an alcohol treatment unit may be necessary. Medications are mainly used for 'drying out' if you get withdrawal symptoms. It is important to avoid relying on tranquillisers as an alternative.

Anyone who drinks can develop an alcohol problem – and some people lose everything – alcohol is a major cause of homelessness. Although some people may just need support and to talk, others may need longer-term help so that they can get somewhere to live, start to make relationships again and get back to work.

Tackling your alcohol problem can be hard work, but it pays off in the end by making a difference across all aspects of your life.

How much alcohol is too much?

Some drinks are stronger than others. The easiest way to work out how much we are drinking is to count 'units' of alcohol. One unit is 10 ml of alcohol – the amount in a standard pub measure of spirits, a half pint of normal strength beer or lager, or a small glass of wine.

If a man and woman of the same weight drink the same amount of alcohol, the woman will have a much higher amount in her bodily organs than the man. So, unfair as it may seem, the safe limit is lower

for women (14 units per week) than for men (21 units per week).

'Binge' drinking

How much you drink at one time is also important. These 'safe limits' assume that our drinking is spread out through the week.

In any one day, it is best for a man to drink no more than four units and for a woman to drink no more than three units. Drinking over eight units in a day for men, or six units for women is known as 'binge drinking'.

You can drink above the safe limit on one night, but still remain within your 'safe' limit for the week. There is some evidence that, even a couple of days of binge drinking, may start to kill off brain cells. This was previously thought only to happen with people who drank continuously for long periods of time. Binge drinking also seems to be connected with an increased risk of early death in middle-aged men.

Guide to units of alcohol

The tables give a rough guide to the amount of alcohol found in different drinks.

These guidelines are approximate and may vary depending on the brand chosen and the size of measure. All alcohol sold in the UK above 1.2% ABV (Alcohol By Volume) should state how strong it is in percentages (%).

The higher the percentage, the more alcohol it has in it. Pub measures are generally rather smaller than the amount we pour ourselves at home.

August 2013

⇨ The above information is reprinted with kind permission from the Royal College of Psychiatrists. Please visit www.rcpsych.ac.uk for further information.

Wines & Spirits	Strength ABV	Small Glass/ Pub Measure	Wine Glass	Bottle 750ml
Table Wine	12–14%	–	1.5–2.5	–
Fortified Wine (Sherry, Martini, Port)	15–20%	0.8	2–3	–
Spirits (Whisky, Vodka, Gin)	40%	1	–	30

The short-term effects of drinking alcohol

Most of us are familiar with the pleasant glow that follows a couple of drinks. But there are other effects that alcohol has on your body and mind which may surprise you.

What happens when you drink?

Within minutes of taking your first sip, alcohol enters your bloodstream through your stomach wall and is circulated to every part of your body, including your heart, liver and brain. It acts on nerve cells throughout your body and slows down the speed at which your nerves send messages to each other.

If you have one or two drinks, you may find you become more talkative and feel more cheerful and relaxed. But drink a couple more and you will take longer to react, you may misjudge situations and may also find that you start slurring your speech. Walking and coordination may also become more difficult.

So what's happening to your mind and body?

The effects of alcohol on your mind

Alcohol is a depressant. Drink too much and your brain will have difficulty processing information. This means you may have trouble with:

⇨ judgement and self-control

⇨ vision and hearing

⇨ talking and walking

⇨ remembering things

⇨ sleeping – you're more likely to wake up during the night and you may have difficulty getting back to sleep again

⇨ anxiety and low mood or depression.

The effects of alcohol on your body

Your liver

Your liver has many functions and one of them is to filter and clean your blood. It takes about one hour for your liver to clear a unit of alcohol from your bloodstream – this is the most your liver can handle at one time, so if you are drinking quickly, your liver has to work much harder. The more you drink, the more you're going to feel the effects of alcohol.

Your stomach

Alcohol irritates your stomach. Alcohol increases the amount of acid your stomach produces. The acid can cause inflammation of your stomach lining. If you drink too much alcohol, you're likely to have indigestion. If you have indigestion, you may have heartburn, feel or be sick, have a stomach ache and have problems with flatulence, burping or belching.

Your heart

Alcohol makes your heart beat faster, which affects how well your heart pumps blood around your body. You may find that drinking alcohol gives you palpitations (arrhythmia). Alcohol can also cause your blood pressure to drop, which may make you feel faint. Drinking a lot of alcohol and binge drinking can cause changes in your blood pressure and increase your risk of a heart attack.

Your kidneys and bladder

Alcohol makes you produce more urine. If you drink too much, your body will try to get rid of the alcohol, mixed with water, in your urine. Not only will you need to make repeat trips to the toilet, but if you don't top up with water or soft drinks, it will leave you feeling thirsty and dehydrated.

Your sexual function

Drinking moderate levels of alcohol can increase your sexual desire and, by reducing tension, enhance your enjoyment. But drink too much and its effects on the nervous system can make it difficult for men to achieve or maintain an erection (often called 'brewer's droop').

Your appearance

Alcohol temporarily dilates (expands) the small blood vessels in your skin and on the surface of your eyes, making them look red. Drink too much and you will have bloodshot eyes, dark circles under your eyes and your skin may be more prone to bruising. Your skin may feel hot and sweaty, and you may smell of alcohol, as some alcohol leaves your body through sweat.

In the cold, the effect of dilated blood vessels in your skin may give you a false illusion of being warm, though the actual temperature of your body can fall, which can lead to hypothermia.

Alcohol contains a lot of calories and can lead to weight gain. It can also make your stomach feel bloated.

'Drinking a lot of alcohol... can cause changes in your blood pressure and increase your risk of a heart attack'

The morning after

The morning after an evening of heavy drinking, you can expect to have a hangover. A hangover is nature's way of telling you that you have overindulged in alcohol. Alcohol contains ethanol – a toxic chemical. It takes time for your body to turn the ethanol into a less toxic substance in your body. Symptoms of a hangover are caused by the combined effects of alcohol and its breakdown products on your body and mind. Typical symptoms include:

⇨ a pounding head

⇨ feeling thirsty

⇨ feeling sick

⇨ sensitivity to bright lights and loud noises

⇨ red eyes and a dry, bloated and puffy face

⇨ indigestion and mild diarrhoea

⇨ tiredness and weakness.

Worse still, you may not even be able to remember aspects of what happened the night before because alcohol can cause memory loss.

Are you drinking too much?

If you binge drink, which generally means drinking over twice the daily recommended amount in one session, you're likely to feel ill and may get into situations where you are vulnerable or risk harming yourself or others through accidents, injuries and misjudgement. If you really overdo it, you're likely to vomit and/or pass out. This may result in problems with breathing and can even be fatal, for example if you pass out and inhale vomit. If you drink too much in a short space of time, the amount of alcohol in your bloodstream can become dangerously high. This can lead to alcohol poisoning and you will need urgent hospital treatment.

If you're struggling to keep within your limits, don't be afraid to talk to someone. Talking to a close friend, a support group or your GP can help you understand your drinking habits and find ways to cut down how much you drink.

December 2012

⇨ The above information is reprinted with kind permission from the Bupa Health Information Team. Please visit www.bupa.co.uk for further information.

Long-term effects

As well as the recognised immediate effects of drinking too much, such as nausea and vomiting, binge drinking and prolonged heavy drinking over longer periods of time can affect you in many different ways.

Brain damage

Binge drinking can cause blackouts, memory loss and anxiety. Long-term drinking can result in permanent brain damage, serious mental health problems and alcohol dependence or alcoholism. Young people's brains are particularly vulnerable because the brain is still developing during their teenage years. Alcohol can damage parts of the brain, affecting behaviour and the ability to learn and remember.

Cancers

Drinking alcohol is the second biggest risk factor for cancers of the mouth and throat (smoking is the biggest). People who develop cirrhosis of the liver (often caused by too much alcohol) can develop liver cancer.

Heart and circulation

Alcohol can cause high blood pressure (hypertension), which increases the risk of having a heart attack or stroke. It also weakens heart muscles, which can affect the lungs, liver, brain and other body systems, and also cause heart failure. Binge drinking and drinking heavily over longer periods can cause the heart to beat irregularly (arrhythmia) and has been linked to cases of sudden death.

Lungs

People who drink a lot of alcohol have more lung infections, are more likely to suffer collapsed lungs and can be more likely to get pneumonia. When a person vomits as a result of drinking alcohol, they may choke if vomit gets sucked into their lungs.

Liver

Drinking too much alcohol initially causes fat deposits to develop in the liver. With continued excessive drinking, the liver may become inflamed, causing alcoholic hepatitis, which can result in liver failure and death. Excessive alcohol can permanently scar and damage the liver, resulting in liver cirrhosis and an increased risk of liver cancer. Women are particularly susceptible to the effects of alcohol on the liver.

Stomach

Drinking above recommended limits can lead to stomach ulcers, internal bleeding and cancer. Alcohol can cause the stomach to become inflamed (gastritis), which can prevent food from being absorbed and increase the risk of cancer.

Pancreas

Heavy or prolonged use of alcohol can cause inflammation of the pancreas, which can be very painful – causing vomiting, fever and weight loss – and can be fatal.

Intestine

Heavy drinking may result in ulcers and cancer of the colon. It also affects your body's ability to absorb nutrients and vitamins.

Alcohol: units and calories

Bottle of red wine	250 ml glass of red wine	Lager pint	Spirit shot	Gin & tonic
(13% vol)	(13% vol)	(5% vol)	(40% vol)	(37.5% vol)
600 cal	200 cal	233 cal	61 cal	108 cal
9.8 units	3.3 units	2.8 units	1 unit	0.9 units

Kidneys

Heavy drinking can increase your risk of developing high blood pressure – a leading cause of chronic kidney disease.

Fertility

In men: impotence (lowered libido/sex drive) and infertility. In women: infertility.

Drinking alcohol when pregnant can seriously damage the development of the unborn baby.

Bones

Alcohol interferes with the body's ability to absorb calcium. As a result, your bones become weak and thin (osteoporosis).

Weight gain

Alcohol is high in calories. Weight for weight, the alcohol in a drink contains almost as many calories as fat. The average bottle of wine contains 600 calories while four pints of average strength lager contain 640.

Skin

Alcohol dehydrates your body and your skin. It also widens blood vessels, causing your skin to look red or blotchy.

Sexual health

Binge drinking makes you lose your inhibitions and affects your judgement. This may make you less likely to use a condom, which increases your risk of getting a sexually transmitted infection such as chlamydia, HIV or hepatitis. It can also lead to an unplanned pregnancy.

Mental health

People may think that alcohol helps them cope with difficult situations and emotions, and that it reduces stress or relieves anxiety, but alcohol is in fact associated with a range of mental health problems including depression, anxiety, risk-taking behaviour, personality disorders and schizophrenia.

Alcohol has also been linked to suicide. The Mental Health Foundation reports that:

⇨ 65% of suicides have been linked to excessive drinking;

⇨ 70% of men who take their own life drink alcohol before doing so;

⇨ almost one third of suicides among young people take place while the person is intoxicated.

Excessive drinking can disrupt normal sleeping patterns, resulting in insomnia and a lack of restful sleep, which can contribute to stress and anxiety.[1]

Other effects

Alcohol affects the parts of your brain that control judgement, concentration, coordination, behaviour and emotions. If you binge drink, you may be at greater risk of:

⇨ becoming a victim of crime, e.g. rape, domestic violence, mugging or assault;

⇨ being involved in anti-social or criminal behaviour, e.g. fights, domestic violence, vandalism or theft;

⇨ having an accident, e.g. a road accident, fall, accident at work or accidental fire;

⇨ losing your job, e.g. repeated absence or poor performance (think about the financial consequences);

⇨ damaging relationships with family or friends.

If you want to enjoy a drink, try to stay within recommended limits.

⇨ The above information is reproduced with kind permission from the Public Health Agency, Northern Ireland. Please visit www.knowyourlimits.info or www.publichealth.hscni.net for further information.

© Public Health Agency 2013

Where's the booze?

Where's your brain?

1 Mental Health Foundation. Cheers! Understanding the relationship between alcohol and mental health. London: Mental Health Foundation, 2006.

Alcohol poisoning – prevention

Alcohol passes quickly into your bloodstream. The physical and mental effects on your body can happen very suddenly.

To stop yourself from getting drunk and risking alcohol poisoning, it helps to be aware of how much you are drinking and the effect this could have on your body.

The effects of alcohol

Around 1–2 units

⇨ your heart rate will speed up and your blood vessels expand

⇨ you get the warm, sociable feeling associated with moderate drinking

Around 4–6 units

⇨ your decision making and judgement will start to be affected, making you lose your inhibitions and become more reckless

⇨ the cells in your nervous system will start to be affected, making you feel light-headed

⇨ your coordination will be affected and your reaction time may be slower

Around 8–9 units

⇨ your reaction times will be much slower

⇨ your speech will begin to slur

⇨ your vision will begin to lose focus

⇨ your liver will be unable to remove all of the alcohol overnight, so it is likely you will wake up with a hangover

At this stage you should seriously consider not drinking any more alcohol.

But if you do:

Around 10–12 units

⇨ your coordination will be seriously impaired, placing you at high risk of having an accident

⇨ you may stagger around or feel unstable on your feet

⇨ you will feel drowsy or dizzy

⇨ the amount of alcohol in your body will begin to reach toxic (poisonous) levels

⇨ you may need to go to the toilet more often as your body attempts to quickly pass the alcohol out with your urine

⇨ you will be dehydrated in the morning, and probably have a severe headache

⇨ the excess alcohol in your system may upset your digestive system, leading to nausea, vomiting, diarrhoea or indigestion

More than 12 units

⇨ you're at high risk of developing alcohol poisoning, particularly if you are drinking lots of units in a short space of time

⇨ the alcohol can begin to interfere with the automatic functions of your body, such as your breathing, heart rate and gag reflex

⇨ you are at risk of losing consciousness

Some tips for drinking less

⇨ Replace some of your drinks with non-alcoholic or low-alcohol drinks.

⇨ If you drink mainly when you go out, try going out later or having your first drink later.

⇨ If you drink mainly at home, trying buying non-alcoholic or low-alcohol alternatives.

⇨ Buy smaller glasses and watch how much you pour.

⇨ If you enjoy drinking pints in the pub or cans of beer watching football, remember lower-strength lagers and beers are available.

⇨ If you use alcohol to 'wind down' after a hard day, find alternatives, such as exercise classes or relaxation techniques.

⇨ Avoid drinking on an empty stomach.

⇨ Avoid mixing different alcoholic drinks, such as beer with wine, or spirits with beer.

Keeping a drink diary

If you are not sure how much you are drinking on a daily basis, try keeping a drink diary. Every day, make a note of:

⇨ all the alcoholic drinks you had

⇨ how many units you drank

⇨ what time you had them

⇨ where you were.

This should give you a good idea of how much you are drinking, the situations in which you drink and where you could start to cut down.

15 June 2012

⇨ The above information is reprinted with kind permission from NHS Choices. Please visit www.nhs.uk for further information.

© NHS Choices 2012

Alcohol dependence

Alcohol dependency is a condition that is marked by an overpowering urge to drink alcohol. It's more common in people who have anxiety, depression or a lot of stress in their lives.

About alcohol dependence

Alcohol is an addictive drug and although many people drink safely, you can become psychologically and physically dependent on it. In the UK, around nine in 100 men and four in 100 women show signs of being dependent on alcohol.

Alcohol dependence – or 'alcohol dependence syndrome' (formerly known as alcoholism) – is a pattern of routinely drinking excessive amounts of alcohol over a long period of time, and giving priority to drinking over other activities and obligations in your life. It can cause or worsen psychological and physical health problems and can seriously affect your relationships with family and friends. It can also affect your job, or result in drinking-related offences.

Symptoms of alcohol dependence

The main symptom of alcohol dependence is having an overpowering urge to drink alcohol and not being able to limit or stop drinking once you have started. Some people who are dependent on alcohol report being preoccupied with it and that the need to drink alcohol takes over their lives.

If you drink regularly, your body gets used to lots of alcohol and you may find that you need to drink increasingly more to feel its effects. This is known as alcohol tolerance and has a role in you becoming addicted to alcohol.

Other symptoms of alcohol dependence can include:

⇨ neglecting other interests in favour of pursuits that involve alcohol

⇨ spending more time drinking and recovering from the effects of alcohol than you used to

⇨ drinking before midday

⇨ anxiety or irritability

⇨ feeling that you can't cut down on your drinking despite signs that it's damaging your health, your personal relationships or your work.

You don't necessarily need to have all of these symptoms to be affected by alcohol dependence, and any of the above can indicate that there is a problem.

Another sign that you're dependent on alcohol is if you have physical withdrawal symptoms when you stop drinking. You may feel the need to drink to avoid or relieve such symptoms. Withdrawal symptoms include:

⇨ shaking or tremors

⇨ feeling or being sick first thing in the morning

⇨ sweating a lot

⇨ finding it difficult to sleep

⇨ feeling your heart race

⇨ anxiety or irritability.

Complications of alcohol dependence

If you drink large amounts of alcohol, you're at greater risk of having:

⇨ liver disease (such as fatty liver, alcoholic hepatitis or alcoholic cirrhosis)

⇨ high blood pressure and other heart problems (such as heart muscle damage, heart disease and stroke)

⇨ cancer (such as cancer of your liver, throat, mouth, bowel, oesophagus and breast)

⇨ memory loss

⇨ depression

⇨ suicidal feelings

⇨ problems with your sex life or fertility

⇨ dementia

⇨ pancreatitis

⇨ damage to your nerves (neuropathy).

Another potential complication is delirium tremens, which can happen if you stop drinking immediately rather than cutting down gradually. This causes symptoms such as shaking, sweating, diarrhoea and seizures. It may also cause anxiety, confusion, paranoia and hallucinations (where you see and/or hear things that aren't there). Delirium tremens requires urgent medical attention as it can be life threatening.

If you're pregnant and drink alcohol, it can affect the development of your unborn baby and may cause him or her to have a condition called foetal alcohol syndrome. Drinking during pregnancy can also increase your chance of having a miscarriage.

Causes of alcohol dependence

There isn't one main cause of alcohol dependence. People drink alcohol for many different reasons. You may, for example, use alcohol as a way of dealing with anxiety and depression. However, although it may help you dismiss your problems in the short term, alcohol actually makes anxiety and depression worse because it interacts with chemicals called neurotransmitters in your brain that alter your mood.

Social factors, such as the affordability and availability of alcohol, peer pressure and the buying of rounds in groups may have a role in causing alcohol dependency.

Alcohol dependence can run in families – if one of your parents is dependent on alcohol, you're four times more likely to develop it too.

Diagnosis of alcohol dependence

Acknowledging that alcohol has a negative impact on your life is an important first step to get the help and support that is available. If you feel that you may be dependent on alcohol, see your GP. He or she will ask about your symptoms and may examine you. Your GP may also ask you about your medical history.

Your GP will ask about your drinking, how you feel about it and its effect on your life and well-being. He or she may ask you some specific questions that are listed in questionnaires, which aim to establish if you're alcohol dependent. Examples of these questionnaires include the alcohol use disorders identification test (AUDIT) and severity of alcohol dependence questionnaire (SADQ).

If your lifestyle, psychological or physical illness or the score on one of the questionnaires indicate you may be drinking too much, your GP may refer you to specialist alcohol services. In most areas in the UK, you can self-refer to some alcohol services too. If your problem is less severe, your GP may give you advice or offer written information aimed at preventing you from developing problems in the future.

Treatment of alcohol dependence

Your treatment will be tailored to suit you and will depend on how much you drink, and if you have any physical or mental health problems.

Your GP will assess your level of alcohol dependence. If you have severe alcohol dependence, especially if there is evidence of physical damage to your internal organs such as your liver, then your GP is likely to advise you to cut down on alcohol with the aim of stopping drinking completely. This is called abstinence.

However, there are people with a lower level of alcohol use or who may not be willing to give up alcohol completely for whom controlled drinking might be a possibility. It's important to work with your GP to agree on a treatment plan that is realistic for you, and which you can stick to. It may be that you aim to cut down your drinking to a controlled, lower level.

There are professional services and groups that can give you help and support to stop drinking.

Self-help

Acknowledging that you're dependent on alcohol and finding the determination to change and the willpower to do so is important for your treatment to be a success. There are a number of self-help tools such as information leaflets and websites that can help you to stop drinking. These tools should normally be used in addition to help from a healthcare professional or voluntary agency.

Detoxification

If you're a heavy drinker, you may need to be supervised by health professionals while you give up alcohol (assisted alcohol withdrawal). This is because the physical withdrawal symptoms associated with stopping drinking can carry health risks. Detoxification or 'detox' is a planned withdrawal from drinking alcohol and may involve taking a short course of a medicine to help prevent withdrawal symptoms. Benzodiazepine medicines, such as diazepam or chlordiazepoxide, are most commonly used during detoxification. Your GP may prescribe these for you to take at home or you may need to stay in a specialist treatment centre during detoxification. You will gradually take less and less of the medicine until you can stop altogether – medicines are only a short-term treatment to help you gain control and not a long-term solution.

Counselling

You might find that talking to someone about your drinking problem is a useful and important part of your treatment. You may wish to speak to your GP or trained counsellors who can help you understand the reasons for your drinking, and give you skills to control or stop the urge to drink.

Your partner or family may also be invited to attend counselling with you and be involved in your treatment.

Mutual help support groups

There are a number of support groups in the UK where you can share personal experiences and advice with other people who are dependent on alcohol. Mutual help support groups can help you while you're giving up and can also help prevent you becoming dependent again. Support groups such as Alcoholics Anonymous and Al-Anon (a support group for family and friends of those who are alcohol dependent) are found nationwide.

Dietary supplements

You may be deficient in vitamins and minerals due to your alcohol intake; vitamin B1 (thiamine) deficiency is common, for example. Your GP may prescribe thiamine tablets and ask you to take multivitamins.

Preventing a relapse

If you successfully give up drinking, starting again (or relapsing) is common. There are a number of ways that you can plan ahead and minimise the risks of this happening to you. It's important to remember that treatment for alcohol dependence is an ongoing process. You're more likely to successfully give up drinking if you receive help and support from family and friends, mutual help support groups, your GP or from a counsellor.

There are medicines that your GP may prescribe that can help prevent your cravings for alcohol (such as acamprosate) or other medicines (such as disulfiram), which help deter you from drinking by giving you unpleasant symptoms such as vomiting and a headache if you drink alcohol.

June 2012

⇨ The above information is reprinted with kind permission from the Bupa Health Information Team. Please visit www.bupa.co.uk for further information.

Alcohol dependency prescriptions up three quarters in a decade

Prescriptions to treat alcohol dependency have risen by 73 per cent in a decade, according to figures from the Health and Social Care Information Centre (HSCIC). More than 178,000 prescriptions were issued in 2012, compared to just under 168,000 the previous year and fewer than 103,000 in 2003.

The 2012 figure is the highest number ever recorded by HSCIC, with a net ingredient cost of £2.93 million, says *Statistics on alcohol: England, 2013*. The report illustrated the impact of alcohol misuse on hospitals in England, according to HSCIC.

'It is extremely important that patients who are dependent on alcohol have access to drugs that can help them recover,' said Royal College of Physicians advisor on alcohol, Dr Nick Sheron. 'However, the rise in prescriptions of drugs to treat alcohol dependency is indicative of the huge strain alcohol abuse puts on our society.'

While the report looked at the number of prescriptions being used to treat dependency, the 'real issue' was 'the vast numbers of people who are not getting help for their alcohol addiction', said Alcohol Concern's director of campaigns, Emily Robinson. The charity estimated that just one in 16 people with an alcohol problem received specialist help, as 'there is just not enough treatment available', she said.

Meanwhile, a report from the National Confidential Enquiry into Patient Outcome, and Death has concluded that patients with alcohol-related liver disease are being failed by some hospitals. *Measuring the Units: A review of patients who died with alcohol-related liver disease* calls for all patients presenting to hospital to be screened for alcohol misuse, and all those presenting to acute services with a history of potentially harmful drinking referred to alcohol support services for 'a comprehensive physical and mental assessment', with the results sent to their GP. It also recommends that a consultant-led multidisciplinary alcohol care team be established in every acute hospital.

'The first thing I found surprising was how many of these extremely ill people were admitted under doctors who claimed no specialist knowledge of their disease, and how many of them were not then seen by an appropriate specialist within a reasonable period,' said NCEPOD chair Bertie Leigh.

'As well as raising standards of care for these patients, we need to make sure we can intervene earlier to prevent this shocking loss of young lives,' said chair of Alcohol Health Alliance UK, Sir Ian Gilmore.

Statistics on alcohol: England, 2013 at www.hscic.gov.uk.

8 July 2013

⇨ The above information is reprinted with kind permission from Drink and Drugs News (DDN). Please visit www.drinkanddrugsnews.com for further information.

Sensible drinking

A drink or two may help you to relax and socialise and it may even do you some good, but regularly overdoing it is associated with various health risks. Sensible drinking involves knowing what your limits are and being aware of how much you're drinking and your pattern of alcohol use. It's important to understand how to drink sensibly to enjoy alcohol in moderation as part of a healthy lifestyle.

About alcohol

Drinking within safe limits is unlikely to do you any harm and it's even been suggested that for certain people, a small amount of alcohol – that is about one or two units of alcohol a day – may be good for your heart. But in truth, there are more effective ways to protect your heart, including eating a healthy balanced diet and taking regular exercise.

If you regularly drink too much alcohol, not only do you risk your health, but depending on how much and how often you drink, your work and relationships may also be affected.

To stay safe and healthy, it pays to know your limits and drink alcohol sensibly.

What are sensible drinking limits?

The Department of Health guidelines recommend not regularly drinking more than:

⇨ three or four units a day for men

⇨ two or three units a day for women.

'Regularly' means every day or most days of the week. This does not mean you can save up all the 'allowance' for a weekend binge. A drinking binge is generally defined as drinking double the daily recommended units in one session. Binge drinking for men, therefore, is drinking more than eight units of alcohol – or about three pints of strong beer. For women, it's drinking more than six units of alcohol – the equivalent of two large glasses of wine.

Why are sensible drinking limits different for women?

The recommended limits are lower for women than for men because women have different amounts of fat, muscle and water in their bodies than men. This affects the way women and men's bodies cope with alcohol. As a result, women are more likely to develop health problems, such as liver disease, at lower levels of alcohol consumption than men.

How many units in your drink?

The UK aims to state on the label of all alcohol drinks how much alcohol they contain. This is expressed as 'percentage alcohol by volume' (% ABV). The packaging should also give the number of units of alcohol the drink contains.

One unit is equal to 10 ml by volume or 8 g by weight, of pure alcohol – the amount of alcohol an average adult can process in one hour. The number of units of alcohol in different drinks varies, for example:

⇨ one 25 ml single measure of spirit (37.5% ABV) is equal to one unit

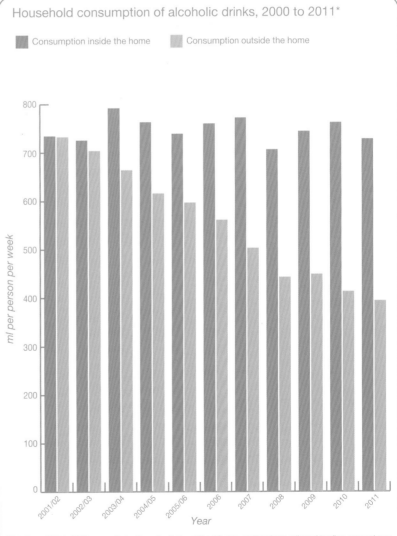

Household consumption of alcoholic drinks, 2000 to 2011*

■ Consumption inside the home   ■ Consumption outside the home

y-axis: ml per person per week

x-axis: Year — 2001/02, 2002/03, 2003/04, 2004/05, 2005/06, 2006, 2007, 2008, 2009, 2010, 2011

*Data from 1992 to 2000 was collected from the National Food Survey and has been adjusted to allow comparisons to data collected from 2001/02 to 2007 from the Expenditure and Food Survey (EFS). In 2008 the EFS was renamed the Living Costs and Food Survey (LCFS) when it became part of the Integrated Household Survey. The data presented here comes from the Family Food Module of LCFS.

Source: Statstics on Alcohol - England, 2013. Health & Social Care Information Centre.

⇨ a 175 ml (standard) glass of red wine (12% ABV) is equal to two units

⇨ a pint of beer (4% ABV) contains 2.3 units

⇨ a pint of cider (4.5% ABV) contains 2.6 units.

Be aware that alcoholic drinks vary in strength; for example, some wines and lagers contain more alcohol than others. What's more, bars and restaurants offer a variety of measures, such as spirits in measurements of 25, 35 or 50 ml, and wine glass measurements of 125, 175 or 250 ml. So, for instance, if you drink three glasses of 250 ml wine, you're drinking a whole bottle of wine and three times the recommended amount. It can be easy to do without even realising it.

In fact, some research has shown that only one in eight adults keep track of their drinking and most people aren't clear about the relationship between units, alcohol strengths and glass sizes. Another survey found that around three in ten adults drink more than the recommended amount of alcohol on at least one day each week.

To accurately track how many units you are drinking, try our alcohol units calculator. There are also apps for your phone that can help you keep track.

Drinking sensibly

Drinking sensibly doesn't mean missing out on all the fun. The first steps are to understand how much and how often you're drinking. Start by keeping a record of how much you drink over a week. You may find you're drinking within your limits and don't need to change your drinking habits. But if you're exceeding your safe limits, think about when and where you're drinking and how much. You may be having a glass of wine with most evening meals, a lunchtime drink once a week and a planned night out every Friday or Saturday. Remembering a few simple tips can help you drink sensibly.

⇨ Have something to eat before you drink, and if possible, while you're drinking – this slows down how quickly your body absorbs alcohol.

⇨ Start with low-alcohol or alcohol-free drinks, or alternate these with alcoholic drinks. You could also switch to a lower alcoholic drink.

⇨ Pace yourself – enjoy your drink slowly. Don't drink in rounds or you may be drinking at a much faster pace.

⇨ Buy yourself an alcohol measure for your home so that you can see how much you're putting in your drink. Keep track with an alcohol app when you're out on the town.

⇨ Instead of going to the pub or having a drink at home, try going to the gym or doing another activity you enjoy such as having a bath.

⇨ Don't drink alcohol every day of the week – have at least two alcohol-free days.

When not to drink?

It takes about one hour for your liver to break down one unit of alcohol. The more you drink, the longer it will take for the effects of alcohol to clear. There are times when not drinking alcohol at all is the safest choice. These include the following.

⇨ Before you plan to drive or when you're driving.

⇨ Before or when you're operating machinery or electrical equipment.

⇨ Before or during swimming or other active sports.

⇨ When you're taking certain medicines – always read the patient information leaflet that comes with your medicine and ask your GP or pharmacist for advice.

⇨ When you're pregnant or trying for a baby. Drinking alcohol during pregnancy can increase the risk of miscarriage and affect the development of your unborn baby.

Do you need help cutting down?

If you're struggling to keep within your limits, don't be afraid to talk to someone. Talking to a close friend, a support group or your GP can help you understand your drinking habits and find ways to cut down how much you drink.

December 2012

⇨ The above information is reprinted with kind permission from the Bupa Health Information Team. Please visit www.bupa.co.uk for further information.

The dangers of fake alcohol

The dangers of drinking fake alcohol, how to recognise it, and what to do if you see fake alcohol being sold.

In recession-hit Britain, producing fake alcohol has been seen as a way of making money, and it's sold cheaply. But it's a problem because of the risks it poses to people's health, causing anything from nausea to blindness and even death.

What is fake alcohol?

Fake or illegally produced alcohol is alcohol that is produced in unlicensed distilleries or people's homes and intended for sale. It is illegal to distil and sell alcohol to the public in the UK without a licence from HM Revenue & Customs (HMRC). Since 2005, HMRC has seized nearly 15 million litres of illegally produced alcohol. They've also prosecuted 15 major criminal gangs involved in producing alcohol and not paying tax on it.

Meanwhile, Trading Standards Institute officers have reported an increase in fake or illegally produced alcohol being sold in the UK during 2011, much of which contained potentially dangerous chemicals.

'We're very concerned about this trend in the availability of fake alcohol,' says Ron Gainsford, Chief Executive of the Trading Standards Institute. 'It's not just about false bargains, counterfeit spirits and wine could be lethal.'

Health risks from fake alcohol

Properly produced and certified alcoholic drinks are made with ethanol – alcohol that's safe to drink in moderation. But fake alcoholic drinks can be produced using other cheaper types of alcohol which can have serious adverse effects on your health. Drinkaware's Chief Medical Advisor Professor Paul Wallace explains: 'Commonly used substitutes for ethanol include chemicals used in cleaning fluids, nail polish remover and automobile screen wash, as well as methanol and isopropanol which are used in antifreeze and some fuels. These other types of alcohol can produce similar effects to ethanol in terms of making you feel tipsy. But they are also potentially very dangerous.'

Drinking alcohol containing these chemicals can cause nausea and vomiting, abdominal pain, drowsiness and dizziness. Drinking it can lead to kidney or liver problems and even coma. Methanol, the substance recently found in fake vodka, can cause permanent blindness.

'Drinking illegally produced alcohol should be avoided at all costs,' says Dr Wallace. 'You don't know what's in it in terms of the actual chemicals – and you don't know the strength of what you're drinking because it's not been produced to the standards of commercial alcohol.'

How to recognise fake alcohol

Jeremy Beadles, former Chief Executive of the Wine and Spirits Trade Association, believes most consumers won't come across fake alcohol and says that it's important to keep the problem in perspective. 'The vast majority of alcohol in the UK is produced and sold legitimately,' he says. 'Most pubs, corner shops, off licences and other retailers are completely legitimate businesses and wouldn't get involved with it.'

However, it's important to know how to spot – and avoid – fake alcohol if you do come across it. According to the Trading Standards Institute, people need to remember 'the 4 Ps': Place, Price, Packaging and Product.

1. Place: Make sure you buy from a reputable supermarket, off licence or shop.

2. Price: If a deal looks too good to be true, it most probably is.

3. Packaging: Look out for:

   ⇨ Poor quality labelling, including things like spelling mistakes.

   ⇨ UK duty stamp – spirits in bottles 35 cl or larger and 30% ABV or higher have to have a duty stamp, which indicates that tax has either been paid or is due to be paid on the contents of the bottle. They're usually incorporated into the label or stuck on the glass. If it's not there, it's illegal.

   ⇨ Properly sealed caps. If the seal is broken, don't drink it. Even if it's not illegal, it could have been tampered with.

   ⇨ Fake bar codes. If you have an app on your mobile that scans bar codes, scan it and see if it's listed as the correct product.

4. Product: Look out for fake versions of well-known brands and be wary of unusual brand names you haven't seen before. Vodka, the most commonly counterfeited spirit, shouldn't have any white particles or sediment in the bottle. If you see this, the vodka could have been diluted with tap water. If any alcohol tastes or smells bad, don't drink it. Particularly look out for the smell of nail varnish.

What to do if you spot fake alcohol

If you think you've drunk fake alcohol, the best thing to do is to seek medical advice. You can also report it to your local environmental health officer, call Consumer Direct on 08454 04 05 06 or the Customs Hotline on 0800 59 5000.

September 2013

⇨ The above information is reprinted with kind permission from Drinkaware. Please visit www.drinkaware.co.uk for further information.

Hospital admissions linked to alcohol rise to more than a million in year

Doctors repeat call for alcohol pricing rule to deter heavy drinkers as Alcohol Concern warns of lack of help for addiction.

By James Meikle

An estimated 1.22 million hospital admissions in England were linked to drinking too much alcohol in 2011–12, according to NHS figures – a 51% rise over the past nine years.

Drug prescriptions to treat alcohol dependency outside hospital are also continuing to rise. Nearly 180,000 prescriptions were dispensed by doctors, nurses and pharmacists in 2012, 6% up in a year and nearly 75% more than in 2003.

Hospital admissions for which drink was the main cause rose to 200,900 in 2011–12, 1% more than the previous year, and more than 40% up on 2002–03.

Men accounted for three in five of the patients whose alcohol consumption was the main reason for admission. Admission rates were highest in north-west England and lowest in the east.

The bleak figures prompted doctors to call again for minimum alcohol pricing, which is the subject of a legal battle between the drinks industry and the Scottish Government and is still formally under consideration in England although there is little ministerial appetite for it.

Nick Sheron, adviser on alcohol at the Royal College of Physicians, said the rise in prescriptions of drugs indicated 'the huge strain alcohol abuse puts on our society' but focused on the admissions.

He added: 'Today's statistics show that in 2012, hospitals in England admitted 200,900 cases where the main reason for admission was an alcohol-related condition.

'The rise in alcohol addiction is being driven by cheap alcohol. A minimum unit price for alcohol would effectively tackle this problem. In Canada, a 10% increase in minimum unit price caused a 32% reduction in deaths.

'Our own research in Southampton shows that a minimum unit price of 50p would, on average, cost patients with alcohol dependency and cirrhosis an additional £36 a week.

'The impact on moderate drinkers was less than 30p a week, because these patients simply do not drink the ultra-cheap, ultra-strong booze. Minimum unit pricing is targeted at very heavy drinkers whose families are devastated by the impact that drinking has on their lives.'

Emily Robinson, director of campaigns at the charity Alcohol Concern, said that the Government 'must get a grip and implement measures that will prevent this urgent situation from getting worse … The real issue is the vast numbers of people who are not getting help for their alcohol addiction. We estimate that only one in 16 people with alcohol problems is receiving specialist help as there is just not enough treatment available.'

A Department of Health spokesman said the figures proved alcohol was causing harm to the health of hundreds of thousands of people.

'That is why we are already improving prevention by funding alcohol risk assessments at GPs and encouraging increased access to alcohol liaison nurses in hospitals.

'The alcohol industry has also pledged to take one billion units out of the market by 2015 and we have consulted on a range of options to tackle irresponsible practices and strengthen local licensing powers.'

A British Beer and Pub Association spokesman said: 'Alcohol misuse remains a problem for a minority and is something we must all work to tackle. Nevertheless, key trends are moving in the right direction.'

30 May 2013

⇨ The above information is reprinted with kind permission from *The Guardian*. Please visit www.guardian.co.uk for further information.

Drunk and disorderly?
Pay to stay in the 'drunk tank'

Drinkers who can't look after themselves should be put in privately-run cells until they sober up – and then pay a fee for the privilege, says a police chief, fed-up with intoxicated revellers.

Chief Constable Adrian Lee, the national policing leader on alcohol harm, said that people who need medical treatment after excess drinking should no longer be the responsibility of the police service.

Launching a week-long campaign aimed at highlighting alcohol harm, Mr Lee suggested that intoxicated individuals be taken to a cell run by a commercial company and charged for their care the morning after.

'I do not see why the police service or the health service should pick up the duty of care for someone who has chosen to go out and get so drunk that they cannot look after themselves,' he said.

'So why don't we take them to a drunk cell owned by a commercial company and get the commercial company to look after them during the night until they are sober?

'When that is over we will issue them with a fixed penalty and the company will be able to charge them for their care, which would be at quite significant cost and that might be a significant deterrent.

It is believed the suggested fee paid to the private company could be in the region of a few hundred pounds.

Nearly 50 per cent of all violent crime is alcohol related, said Acpo.

Private policing

He also criticised the Government for dropping plans to implement a minimum price for a unit of alcohol in England and Wales.

The chief constable is not the first to suggest introducing drunk tanks in the UK: Humberside Police and Crime Commissioner (PCC) Matthew Grove recently suggested

the idea in an interview. And the holding cells for drunks are also used in parts of Europe and America.

The public suggestion comes amid a Government-wide review of all contracts held by Serco and G4S, two of the country's biggest private providers of public services. The audit, triggered by revelations that both firms had overcharged the Government for criminal-tagging contracts, prompted calls for the Ministry of Justice to abandon plans to privatise large chunks of the probation and prison service.

And it follows proposals for increased privatisation of the police service by way of sponsorship –

floated earlier this year by Dorset PCC Martyn Underhill.

Mr Lee added: 'We are not the experts on health. It is quite difficult to work out where the best place to put a drunk is. Is it a police station, or do they need to be at a hospital?'

18 September 2013

⇨ The above information is reprinted with kind permission from Channel 4 News. Please visit www.channel4.com/news for further information.

Alcohol-related accidents

Alcohol is one of the leading causes of accidents, from domestic to traffic related. Get the facts here.

Spilling red wine over your friend's pristine white sofa. Breaking another wine glass all over the floor. Tripping up your front steps.

Drinking can make us prone to minor accidents that almost seem part of your average night. But alcohol can be the cause of more serious accidents too.

There are two main things which make this likely. Because it's a depressant, alcohol slows down the brain and affects the body's responses. At the same time, if you've been drinking, you're more likely to take risks. Combined, these reactions increase the chance of accidents happening.

1. The more you drink, the more likely you are to have an accident

'That table looks perfectly safe to dance on.'

'Forgot my keys. I'll just hop over this fence!'

These are just two examples of the more light-hearted side effects of drinking alcohol once euphoria sets in. But the feeling you get when the amount of alcohol in your blood increases can have disastrous consequences too. It can make you underestimate your own abilities and behave recklessly. That road doesn't look as busy, that gap isn't so big and besides, you are an expert long jumper…

As blood alcohol concentration (BAC) rises, so does the risk of accidents. BAC, the amount of alcohol in your breath or blood, is measured in mg of alcohol per 100 ml of blood, or mg%. It's affected by all sorts of factors, including how much alcohol you drink, how fast you drink it, your body size, how much you've eaten, your gender and even your emotional health.

2. Alcohol slows you down

Alcohol affects your body's responses. It slows down your brain which means you are more likely to have an accident.

Drinking alcohol can:

⇨ affect our judgement and reasoning

⇨ slow down our reactions

⇨ upset our sense of balance and coordination

⇨ impair our vision and hearing

⇨ make us lose concentration and feel drowsy.

3. More young men die from drink driving than any other group of people

Accidents involving drink driving have decreased hugely over the last 30 years. Deaths and serious injuries related to drink driving have fallen by more than three-quarters since 1980.

That's the good news.

The bad news is that traffic accidents are still a leading cause of alcohol-related deaths among young men aged 16 to 24. In 2010, nearly 10,000 reported road casualties happened when a driver was over the legal alcohol limit representing 5% of all road casualties.

For drivers, alcohol can:

⇨ reduce your ability to see distant objects – night vision can be reduced by 25%

⇨ make you have blurred and double vision

⇨ reduce your ability to perceive what is happening around you

⇨ make you lose your peripheral vision.

In the UK, the alcohol limit for drivers is 80 mg of alcohol per 100 ml of blood, 35 mg per 100 ml of breath or 107 mg per 100 ml of urine.

4. Alcohol increases the risk of accidents at home and work, and of accidents involving fires and drownings

Stark statistics reveal the extent to which alcohol increases the risk of accidents of all kinds:

⇨ Accidents at home. Alcohol is the single biggest cause of accidents at home. Of the 4,000 fatal accidents that happen in homes in the UK every year, 400 are alcohol-related.

⇨ Accidents at work. Alcohol is a factor in up to one in four workplace accidents.

⇨ Fires. Around one in three fires are caused by people under the influence of alcohol. And two-thirds of people who are admitted to hospital or die from burns have been drinking.

⇨ Drownings. Between a quarter and half of all adult drowning victims have alcohol in their bloodstream.

5. The effects of alcohol can last longer than you think

Even after alcohol has left your bloodstream, you're more likely to have an accident. In one study, 14 hours after drinking, two-thirds of a group of pilots could not perform routine tasks in a simulator, despite the fact that all the alcohol had left their system. If you've had an accident when you've been drinking, other effects are:

⇨ Your recovery from injury may be hindered. This is because alcohol affects your circulation and the immune system.

⇨ It's harder for doctors to diagnose serious conditions such as head injuries when a patient is drunk.

⇨ Alcohol can interfere with anaesthetic and other medication, meaning operations and treatment may be delayed.

Three ways to avoid alcohol-related accidents

⇨ Don't drive, operate machinery, swim or take unnecessary risks.

⇨ Look out for friends who may be behaving recklessly.

⇨ Remember that your performance and judgement could still be affected by alcohol the day after a heavy drinking session.

Four top first-aid tips to deal with alcohol-related accidents

⇨ If you are at the scene of an accident, call the emergency services as soon as possible. Once you've called for help, if the person who needs it is unconscious, make sure their airway is open. If they are sick and their throat or tongue becomes blocked with vomit, they can choke and stop breathing.

⇨ If the person is breathing, place them in the recovery position. If they aren't breathing, perform chest compressions and breathe into their mouth.

⇨ If someone is bleeding, apply pressure to the wound using a clean cloth or piece of clothing. If they're in shock, lay them down, and raise and support the injured limb.

⇨ If someone is burned or scalded, cool the affected area in cold running water for at least ten minutes, then cover the wound with a clean, non-fluffy cloth to prevent infection.

Alcohol-related accidents facts

⇨ Accident victims who have been drinking suffer more serious injuries than those who haven't.

⇨ Younger people are more likely to have an alcohol-related accident than older people.

⇨ 250 people died because of drink driving accidents in 2010 – 14% of the total number of people who died because of road traffic accidents.

Staying in control

The Government advises that people should not regularly drink more than the daily unit guidelines of three to four units of alcohol for men (equivalent to a pint and a half of 4% beer) and two to three units of alcohol for women (equivalent to a 175 ml glass of wine).

'Regularly' means drinking every day or most days of the week.

Here are three ways you can cut back and keep your drinking under control.

1. Give alcohol-free days a go. If you drink regularly, your body starts to build up a tolerance to alcohol. This is one of the main reasons why it's important to consider taking regular breaks from drinking. Test out having a break for yourself and see what positive results you notice.

2. Stress less. Some people drink alcohol to relax, but in reality alcohol can make you feel even more stressed out. Try not to make alcohol key to your after-work wind down, and consider some alternative stress-busters like hitting the gym or having a hot bath.

3. Know what you're buying. Check out the ABV on a bottle of wine before you buy it. ABV stands for Alcohol By Volume, which is the percentage of the drink that is pure alcohol. It's not uncommon for a bottle of wine to be verging on 15% ABV, which could easily push you over the daily guidelines if you drink more than one glass.

Producers are increasingly introducing 10% or lower ABV wines that are as palatable as their stronger counterparts. Look out for them when you're next buying a bottle.

Further information

Your GP can help you figure out if you should make any changes in your drinking, and offer help and advice along the way.

If you're concerned about someone's drinking, or your own, Drinkline runs a free, confidential helpline. Call 0800 917 8282.

To find out about first-aid courses in your area contact the St John Ambulance on 08700 10 49 50 or via their website www.sja.org.uk.

August 2013

⇨ The above information is reprinted with kind permission from Drinkaware. Please visit www.drinkaware.co.uk for further information.

© 2013 Drinkaware

Is it time for global alcohol consumption guidelines?

A comparison of drinking guidelines around the world shows there is little consensus between countries on what constitutes 'safe' or lower risk alcohol consumption. In this guest post, Dr Richard de Visser, a Senior Lecturer in Psychology at the University of Sussex explores the study conducted with Doctoral student Ms Nina Furtwængler. It was published this month in Drug and Alcohol Review[1].

The study examined Government alcohol consumption guidelines in 57 countries, including all 27 European Member States, and found a remarkable lack of agreement about what constitutes harmful or excessive alcohol consumption on a daily basis or weekly basis.

Key findings were:

⇨ Muslim countries and eight of the 27 EU member states (including Cyprus, Greece and Hungary) do not have readily accessible guidelines. Some countries refer to standard drinks, but do not define them in grams of ethanol (e.g. Kenya, Malta).

⇨ Some countries do not define standard drinks, but offer general guidance encouraging moderate alcohol consumption and/or abstinence in certain circumstances (e.g. Belgium, India, Norway, Western Samoa).

⇨ The alcohol content of a 'unit' or 'standard drink' ranges from 8 g in the UK to 14 g in Slovakia and the USA.

⇨ In some countries the weekly maximum is simply seven times the daily maximum, whereas in others there is an explicit statement that drinkers should have at least one alcohol-free day a week.

⇨ There is no consensus as to whether it is safe for women to drinking as much as men.

Additional analysis of drink-driving legislation found surprisingly wide variation in legal blood and when driving:

⇨ Of the 145 countries for which limits are available, 21 (14%) allow no alcohol in the blood of drivers.

⇨ Among the 124 countries that allow drivers to have alcohol in their blood, there was a ten-fold variation between the least and most generous.

Specific guidelines are likely to be more useful for individuals and health professionals than vague advice to 'drink moderately'. However, it is important to note that people who possess knowledge of unit-based guidelines do not necessarily know how to use them or feel motivated to apply them[2].

Despite these caveats, it is important for people who do want to adhere to recommendations to drink responsibly that there are internationally agreed standard definitions of alcohol units and consumption guidelines. Agreed international guidelines would make it easier for people living in a globalised world to develop and use transferable skills for monitoring and regulating their alcohol consumption.

In England the Government is currently reviewing the drinking guidelines for the first time in 15 years. The Government's response follows the recent House of Commons' Science and Technology Committee (STC) report, which declared the existing guidelines as 'confusing' and called for further clarity.

15 February 2013

⇨ The above information is reprinted with kind permission from Alcohol Policy UK. Please visit www.alcoholpolicy.net for further information.

1. Furtwængler, Nina A. F. F., de Visser, Richard O., 2013. Lack of international consensus in low risk drinking guidelines. Drug and Alcohol Review, *Volume 32 (Issue 1)*, *pages 11–18. Originally published online 4 June 2012.*

2. De Visser, Richard O., Birch, Julian D., 2012. My cup runneth over: Young people's lack of knowledge of low-risk drinking guidelines. Drug and Alcohol Review, *Volume 31 (Issue 2), pages 206–212. Originally published online 3 November 2011.*

Government's response to the alcohol strategy consultation

Oral statement to Parliament.

By Jeremy Browne MP

With permission, Mr Speaker, I shall make a statement on the Government's response to the alcohol strategy consultation. Today we are publishing an analysis of responses to the consultation, along with a 'next steps' document. Copies of both are available in the House Library.

Drunken behaviour and alcohol-fuelled disorder can make towns and cities effective no-go areas for law-abiding people, particularly on Friday and Saturday nights. In nearly 50% of the incidents of violence that took place in 2011–12, the victim believed that the perpetrator was under the influence of alcohol. Excessive alcohol consumption costs the taxpayer huge amounts of money: alcohol-related crime and health harms are estimated to cost society about £21 billion every year. The Government therefore have a role in seeking to curb excessive drinking. We have already increased duty on alcopops, and have introduced a wide-ranging set of reforms to tackle binge drinking.

We want fair and effective policies. We are not in the business of making laws that do not work. For that reason we have consulted widely, and have taken time to consider carefully the representations that we have received and all the relevant arguments. Our response identifies three kinds of action that are necessary. The first is targeted national action: the Government must deal with cheap alcohol, and the alcohol industry must strengthen its voluntary commitments to reduce alcohol-related harms.

There has been much speculation about the government's plans in relation to minimum unit pricing. That policy will remain under consideration, but it will not be proceeded with at this time. We do not yet have enough concrete evidence that its introduction would be effective in reducing harms associated with problem drinking – this is a crucial point – without penalising people who drink responsibly.

We will tackle the most egregious examples of cheap alcohol by banning sales of alcohol below the level of alcohol duty plus value-added tax. That will come into effect in England and Wales no later than the spring of 2014, and will stop the worst instances of deep discounting that result in alcohol being sold cheaply and harmfully. It will no longer be legal to sell a can of ordinary-strength lager for less than about 40p.

We have decided not to ban multi-buy promotions. There is still a lack of convincing evidence that it would have a significant effect in reducing consumption. It would not be reasonable for us to introduce a ban, especially at a time when responsible families are trying hard to balance their household budgets. We will, however, make current mandatory licensing conditions more effective. We will enable tougher action to be taken to deal with irresponsible promotions in pubs and clubs, and will promote responsible drinking by raising customer awareness of the availability of small servings.

Our decision not to proceed with the introduction of minimum unit pricing at this stage gives the alcohol industry an opportunity to demonstrate what more it can do to reduce the harms associated with problem drinking. Our challenge to the industry is to increase its efforts, building on what has already been achieved through the public health responsibility deal. That includes improving education to promote safer drinking, reducing the availability of the high-strength products that cause the most harm for problem drinkers, and responsible marketing and product placement.

Secondly, we intend to facilitate local action. Targeted action by pubs and clubs themselves has proved hugely effective in curbing irresponsible drinking. Best Bar None, National Pubwatch, Purple Flag and community alcohol partnerships are all good examples of what can be achieved when industry works in partnership with local areas. We will build on this by identifying a number of high-harm local alcohol action areas and work with them to strengthen local partnerships, improve enforcement and increase good practice of what works locally, including how areas can make the most of available health data as part of local decision making.

The third area is promoting growth, by freeing up responsible business and community groups from unnecessary red tape, while maintaining the integrity of the licensing system. We will make it quicker and easier for community groups and those wanting to sell small amounts of alcohol as part of a wider service to do so via the community and ancillary seller's notice. We will increase the annual limit for the number of temporary event notices that can apply to a particular premises from 12 to 15, and free up businesses that provide late-night refreshment by removing the requirement to have a licence where there is no need for one. We will abolish the requirement to renew personal licences every ten years. We also plan to consult on whether to abolish personal licences altogether.

Taken together, the Government's response to the alcohol strategy consultation represents a proportionate approach to tackling the worst excesses of alcohol consumption without penalising law-abiding people or responsible businesses. That is the right balance, and I commend this statement to the House.

We will abolish the requirement to renew personal licences every ten years. We also plan to consult on whether to abolish personal licences altogether.

Mr Speaker, taken together the Government's response to the Alcohol Strategy consultation represents a proportionate approach to tackling the worst excesses of alcohol consumption without penalising law-abiding people or responsible businesses. I commend this statement to the House.

17 July 2013

⇨ The above information is reprinted with kind permission from the Home Office. Please visit www.gov.uk for further information.

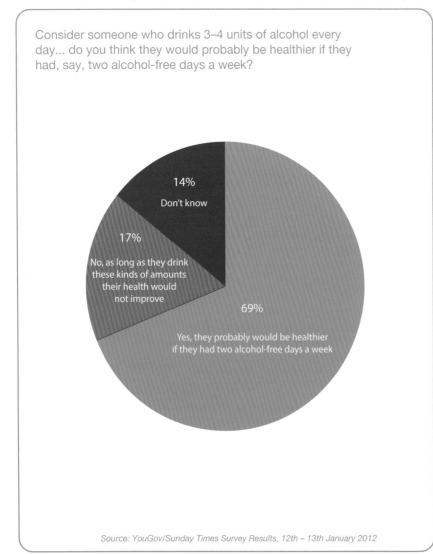

Consider someone who drinks 3–4 units of alcohol every day... do you think they would probably be healthier if they had, say, two alcohol-free days a week?

14%
Don't know

17%
No, as long as they drink these kinds of amounts their health would not improve

69%
Yes, they probably would be healthier if they had two alcohol-free days a week

Source: YouGov/Sunday Times Survey Results, 12th – 13th January 2012

© Crown copyright 2013

Should the legal drinking age be increased to 21?

By Tejvan Pettinger

There are several reasons to be concerned about the over-consumption of alcohol, especially amongst young people. In the UK, abuse of alcohol has contributed to several social, economic and health problems, including:

⇨ Alcohol-related accidents.

⇨ Health problems.

⇨ Alcohol addiction major cause of family breakdown.

According to a report, *Health First: An evidence-based alcohol strategy for the UK*. 'The personal, social and economic cost of alcohol has been estimated to be up to £55 billion per year for England and £7.5 billion for Scotland.'

Research carried out by Sheffield University for the Government shows a 45p minimum would reduce the consumption of alcohol by 4.3%, leading to 2,000 fewer deaths and 66,000 hospital admissions after ten years. Researchers also claim the number of crimes would drop by 24,000 a year.

From an economic perspective, we say that alcohol is a demerit good.

⇨ People may underestimate the personal costs of drinking alcohol to excess (especially amongst young people).

⇨ There are external costs to society, e.g. costs of health care, costs of treating accidents, days lost from work. Therefore the social cost of alcohol is greater than the private cost.

These two factors give a justification for Government intervention to deal with some issues related to alcohol. Raising the legal drinking age could help reduce these personal and social costs because it is more difficult to purchase.

Arguments against raising the drinking age to 21

⇨ At 18, people can vote and are considered adults, so we should allow them to have a personal decision on whether to consume alcohol.

⇨ Alcohol in moderation isn't necessarily harmful. Rather than a blanket ban, the Government could focus on tackling binge drinking through making alcohol more expensive and tackling the drinking culture.

⇨ Drinking alcohol is so embedded in the culture, raising the legal age to 21, will make the majority of young people break the law.

⇨ It will encourage people to find ways to circumnavigate the law. Black market alcohol supplies, which may be harder to monitor.

⇨ Arguably, there are better ways to deal with problems of alcohol.

Will raising the drinking age to 21 be effective?

Raising the drinking age to 21 will reduce consumption amongst young people because it will be harder to buy alcohol. Also, young people are the most likely group to misuse alcohol, e.g. drinking to excess, which causes accidents, death and health problems. If people start drinking later in life, they may be more likely to drink in moderation and not get addicted at an early age.

However, it will still be possible for young people to drink at home. People will find ways to avoid the legislation, e.g. asking older people to buy alcohol for them. Nevertheless, it will be more difficult. For example, a 16-year-old may not be able to get away with drinking in a pub any more. If the age is 18, it is much easier for a 16- or 17-year-old to get away with drinking alcohol.

This policy doesn't address the underlying problem of why people want to drink to excess. For that, education may be a better solution; education could help to explain the dangers of excess drinking and therefore encourage young people to drink in moderation. However, previous education policies have not seemed to be very effective. Young people don't want to hear lectures from the Government about the dangers of alcohol.

Other solutions

Higher taxes increase the cost of alcohol and may have a significant effect in reducing demand amongst young people, who have lower disposable incomes. If demand is reduced by say 20% this may reduce many of the problems of over-consumption. This policy also raises revenue for the Government. But, on the other hand, it may increase the incentive to import low-duty alcohol from abroad. Demand for alcohol may also be inelastic and not effective in stopping consumption.

In practice there is very little that the Government can do to change social and individual attitudes to alcohol, which is the root cause of most alcohol abuse.

In the US the legal drinking age is 21. They still have many alcohol-related problems, but it is significantly more difficult for young people to regularly drink alcohol.

What do you think – should alcohol be illegal for under-21s?

9 May 2013

⇨ The above information is reprinted with kind permission from Economics Help. Please visit www.economicshelp.org for further information.

© Economics Help 2013

Mandatory conditions for alcohol sale: Commons Library Standard Note

A Code of Practice for alcohol retailers containing five mandatory conditions for the sale of alcohol was introduced from April 2010. The Code was the subject of a public consultation exercise in 2009, and the power to introduce it was granted through the Policing and Crime Act 2009. The mandatory conditions:

⇨ ban irresponsible promotions, such as drinking games, speed drinking, 'women drink for free', and 'all you can drink for £10'

⇨ ban pouring drinks directly into the mouths of customers

⇨ ensure free tap water for customers

⇨ ensure that all on trade premises offer small measures of beers, wine and spirits to customers

⇨ ensure that all those who sell or supply alcohol have an age verification policy in place requiring them to ask anyone who looks under 18 for proof of age by providing appropriate identification

The first three conditions came into effect on 6 April 2010. The latter two (age verification policies and smaller measures) came into effect on 1 October 2010.

The alcohol industry had previously had a set of voluntary social responsibility standards in place. However, there was concern that the standards were not consistently adopted and applied across the industry. This, combined with public anxiety about 'binge drinking' and the associated health problems and social harm, led to calls for a mandatory code.

Following a consultation on its alcohol strategy, in July 2013 the Government said that the mandatory conditions would be made more effective, particularly those regulating irresponsible sales and promotions.

September 2013

⇨ The above information is reprinted with kind permission from Parliament UK. Please visit www.parliament.uk for further information.

A nation of 'secret boozers': English people underestimate how much alcohol they drink

Studies show self-reported alcohol consumption accounts for only 40 to 60 per cent of sales.

By John Von Radowitz

England is a nation of secret boozers, with more than a third of the population drinking unhealthy quantities of alcohol, new research suggests.

The finding, which also uncovers high levels of binge drinking, is based on the discrepancy between alcohol sales and the amount people say they drink, in surveys.

International studies show that self-reported alcohol consumption only accounts for between 40 per cent and 60 per cent of sales.

After taking this into account, an estimated 44 per cent of men and 31 per cent of women in England were found to be drinking more than the Royal College of Physicians' safety guidelines for weekly alcohol consumption.

The RCP recommends limits of 21 units of alcohol a week for men and 14 for women. A unit of alcohol is roughly equivalent to half a pint of ordinary strength beer, or nearly one small glass of wine.

Lead researcher Sadie Boniface, from University College London, said: 'Currently we don't know who consumes almost half of all the alcohol sold in England. This study was conducted to show what alcohol consumption would look like when all of what is sold is accounted for, if everyone under-reported equally.

'The results are putative, but they show that this gap between what is seen in the surveys and sales potentially has enormous implications for public health in England.'

The missing alcohol intake increases the prevalence of unhealthy weekly drinking by 15 per cent in men and 11 per cent in women.

Three-quarters of the population were said to be drinking more than the limits for daily consumption recommended by the Department of Health. These are set at four units a day for men and three for women.

After factoring in under-reporting, the study also suggests that around half of all English men and women can be classified as binge drinkers.

Binge drinking is defined by the Department of Health as consuming more than eight units of alcohol in a single session for men, and more than six units for women.

The adjustment pushes up levels of binge drinking most among women, those on high incomes, and people living in the south of England.

The research is published today in the *European Journal of Public Health*.

Ms Boniface's team drew on self-reported data from two major surveys on alcohol consumption conducted in 2008.

The *General Lifestyle Survey* (GLF) recorded average weekly alcohol intake among 12,490 adults in England. Daily consumption was assessed by the *Health Survey for England* (HSE) which examined reported alcohol consumption of 9,608 adults on the heaviest drinking day of the previous week.

'What's needed now is a detailed understanding of whether some people under-report their consumption more than others: to what extent does this vary between men and women for example, by how much someone drinks, or by what types of drink they prefer,' Ms Boniface added.

'Little is known on this at present, but this could reveal groups who under-estimate their alcohol consumption substantially, illuminating areas where targeted alcohol education initiatives should be developed.'

Shadow Public Health Minister Diane Abbott said: 'This has got to be a wake-up call for the Government and the country, because after more than two years of bitter internal rows, the Government has got cold feet about its only proposed alcohol harm policy.

'More needs to be done to tackle problem drinking, which costs the country £21 billion – money we cannot afford.

'I'm absolutely clear that we need to see huge change in our hospitals and high streets – nothing short of a political and cultural earthquake.

'Labour support a minimum unit price but it won't work on its own, and the Government has so far resisted stronger action on prevention.

'Educating young people on the risks of alcohol has been removed from the curriculum and the Government voted against our proposals for stronger licensing powers for local councils to take action in their areas.'

A Department of Health spokesman said: 'We already know people underestimate what they drink and many drink too much. That's why we work to help people make healthier decisions, including the recent Change For Life campaign to help them track consumption and understand the impact on their health.

'We're also tackling excessive drinking through our proposed minimum unit price at 45p per unit, tougher licensing laws, more GP risk assessments, better access to specialist nurses and more specialised treatment.'

27 February 2013

⇨ The above information is reprinted with kind permission from *The Independent*. Please visit www.independent.co.uk for further information.

Percentage of drinkers of each drink who knew what a unit of each type of drink was, 2009

Type of alcohol	Percentage of people who knew what a unit of each drink type was
Beer	63%
Wine	78%
Spirits	69%
Fortified wine	62%
Alcopops	65%

Source: Statstics on Alcohol - England, 2013. Health & Social Care Information Centre.

New figures show UK alcohol consumption down 3.3 per cent in 2012

⇨ UK alcohol consumption per head down again – 3.3 per cent drop in 2012

⇨ 16 per cent decline in consumption per head since 2004

⇨ Per capita consumption below eight litres per head, first time since 1998

New figures for UK alcohol consumption in 2012 show that the amount Britons drink has fallen yet again – for the sixth year out of the past eight. Consumption per head is now 16 per cent lower than it was in 2004 when the current trend began, says the British Beer & Pub Association, which has compiled the new data based on HMRC alcohol tax returns.

2012 was the first year since 1998 that alcohol consumption has dropped below eight litres per head, per year (7.99 litres).

Brigid Simmonds, BBPA Chief Executive, comments:

'Total alcohol consumption is now 16 per cent lower per head than in 2004, when this trend began. While alcohol misuse remains a problem for a minority that we must all work to tackle, it is also important that the debate is fully informed by the latest facts on levels of consumption.'

The data was compiled by the British Beer & Pub Association, from data published on 28 February in the HMRC *Alcohol Bulletin*.

Figures are based on total alcohol released into the UK market, so is not based on sampled or survey data.

The BBPA applies average strengths to wine and cider to establish overall levels in consumption (beer and spirits are already measured in pure alcohol terms), producing data that is widely accepted and used, including by Government sources and the health sector.

The British Beer & Pub Association is the UK's leading organisation representing the brewing and pub sector. Its members account for 96 per cent of the beer brewed in the UK and around half of Britain's 50,000 pubs.

4 March 2013

⇨ The above information is reprinted with kind permission from the British Beer Pub Association. Please visit www.berandpub.com for further information.

Year	Litres of alcohol per head per year	Change year on year
1998	7.96	
1999	8.33	4.5%
2000	8.42	1.1%
2001	8.73	3.7%
2002	9.06	3.8%
2003	9.21	1.6%
2004	9.50	3.2%
2005	9.36	−1.5%
2006	9.05	−3.3%
2007	9.22	1.9%
2008	8.94	−2.5%
2009	8.40	−6.1%
2010	8.44	0.6%
2011	8.26	−2.2%
2012	7.99	−3.3%

Young people who don't drink – not as unusual as you might think

By Mariana Bayley

We are constantly being told that we live in a society where drinking is the norm for young people. Media depictions of young people, women in particular, getting wasted in town centres at weekends would have us believe this. But how accurate a picture is this?

When we began recruiting young people who didn't drink at all or very little for our research we thought we were in for a long haul. How wrong we were! There were more of these young people around than we had imagined and this is indicative of the way false assumptions are shaped by media stereotypes.

Recent survey data explains the ease we found recruiting these young people to our study. Many young people can justifiably complain that the hysteria in the media around drinking is blown out of proportion. Data from the 2010 *General Lifestyle Survey* suggests that 52 per cent of young men aged 16–24 years hadn't drunk alcohol in the previous week and

that this also applies to 54 per cent of young women aged 16–24. So they're actually in the majority and far thicker on the ground than we'd thought! Drinking and getting drunk isn't an automatic rite of passage for young people.

So why would young people choose not to drink alcohol?

Some people just don't like its taste and let's face it most of us have to 'learn' to like alcoholic drinks. Some have seen its destructive effects on families and other people around them. Some have experienced the bad effects of getting drunk themselves and this has prompted them to think again about drinking alcohol. On the other side of the coin, having parents around who are good role models can be a good influence in teaching young people to drink sensibly.

We may well ask how these young people manage their social lives when drinking is such an integral part of going out and having a good time – or is this yet another misplaced assumption? Young people do enjoy

time out without alcohol and for them it's no big deal – just another one of life's choices for many of them – though for others it's more of a statement; an expression of who they are. But surely they must be boring and dull? On the contrary – it's just that much of the time they're involved in activities that don't focus on drinking. When they're not at work or studying, they enjoy doing 'the usual things' like spending time with friends, watching TV, listening to music and so on. Many of them are involved in artwork, writing, sports and other activities – and they want to be able to do these things without a hangover.

Although some avoid drinking establishments altogether, many happily spend time in bars, pubs and clubs like their drinking friends. So how do young people cope with not drinking when they're in a bar or pub? Some are up front about their drinking preferences, while others have nailed down a few simple strategies to help them blend in, such as buying their own drinks, drinking mixers so it looks like they have an alcoholic drink or they'll be driving their drinking friends home.

In a country where diversity is celebrated, let's have a big cheer for diversity in drinking – not drinking needs to be seen as a legitimate choice if that's the choice a young person makes. And let's at least make this an option rather than just assuming everyone is automatically going to drink.

17 August 2012

⇨ The above information is reprinted with kind permission from the Joseph Rowntree Foundation. Please visit www. jrf.org.uk for further information.

Young people underestimate alcohol units, warn researchers

Many young people underestimate how much alcohol they drink even if they have some knowledge of the Government's guidelines on sensible consumption, a study says.

Researchers said their results suggest that young people do not have the knowledge or skills to keep their drinking within the set guidelines.

The University of Sussex-led study, which is published in *Drug and Alcohol Review*, surveyed 18- to 25-year-olds about their knowledge and beliefs on safe drinking.

People who took part in the study were asked to pour their usual measure of wine, beer or vodka followed by what unit they believed it to be.

Nearly two-thirds underestimated the unit content of the drinks they poured, researchers said. The Government's daily unit guidelines are up to two to three units for a woman and up to three to four units for a man.

A pint of lager or cider with a 5% alcohol content contains three units. Two small (125 ml) glasses of wine with a 12% alcohol content are another three units.

Fewer than half of participants in the study gave the correct answer to five out of seven questions testing knowledge of the Government's alcohol consumption guidelines.

But most knew the recommended daily units for men and women.

Research leader Dr Richard de Visser, a senior lecturer in psychology, said: 'Our results indicate that young people tend not to possess the knowledge or skills required to drink alcohol in accordance with Government guidelines.

'Using drink-pouring tasks as part of this education could promote better understanding of alcohol units and more accurate reporting of alcohol consumption.'

A Department of Health spokeswoman said: 'Drinking too much can lead to serious diseases, such as heart disease, cancer and stroke, later in life, so it's really important that we help young people to understand how much they're drinking.

'Earlier this month we launched a new Change4Life campaign about alcohol. It gives us all advice on the health harms and aims to help people who are drinking a bit more than they should to cut down.

'Our forthcoming alcohol strategy will set out our plans on how to deal with the problems and harms alcohol causes.'

The NHS recommends that men should not regularly drink more than three to four units of alcohol a day and women should not regularly drink more than two to three units a day.

Drinking heavily regularly one or two days a week can also harm your long-term health, the NHS says.

27 February 2012

⇨ The above information is reprinted with kind permission from The Press Association. Please visit www. pressassociation.com for further information.

Young people and alcohol

Drinking among young people, in particular excessive drinking, is a major concern for parents, practitioners and the wider community.

There is increasing evidence of the impact drinking is having on young people's long and short-term health, as well as their chances of being in risky situations when drunk. There are also implications for crime and anti-social behaviour as well as for society as a whole.

This article looks at the existing evidence on young people's drinking, showing the prevalence of drinking and highlighting alcohol-related problems that are specific to young people.

Drinking patterns and trends

In recent years there have been significant changes in the way young people drink and how much they drink. Overall the proportion of young people who do not drink is increasing. However among those who do drink, there seems to have been an increase in alcohol consumption:

The proportion of 11–15-year-olds across England who have never drunk alcohol has risen from 38% in 1988 to 49% in 2009

In 2009, over half (51%) of 11–15-year-olds had drunk at least one alcoholic drink in their lifetime. This increases with age from 16% of 11-year-olds to 81% of 15-year-olds.

There has been a decline in the number of 11–15-year-olds who have drunk in the last week. In 2009, 18% of 11–15-year-olds had drunk alcohol at least once a week, down from a peak of 27% in 1996. This is similar for boys and girls. The proportion that had drunk in the last week increases with age from 3% of 11-year-olds to 38% of 15-year-olds. White pupils are more likely to have drunk alcohol recently than Black or Asian pupils.

Of those who drank in the last week, the average weekly consumption has more than doubled since 1990 from 5.3 units a week to 11.4 units per week in 2006. In 2009, 11–15-year-olds who drank in the last week consumed an average of 11.6 units (and a median intake of 7.0 units), equivalent to nearly six pints of normal strength beer or over eight alcopops. (The method used to calculate alcohol consumption changed in 2007 making comparison with pre-2007 consumption levels difficult).

Boys tend to drink more than girls. In 2009, boys who drank in the last week drank more units of alcohol (11.9 units) than girls who drank in the last week (11.3 units). Older pupils who drank in the last week drank more than younger pupils. On average 13.2 units for 15-year-olds, compared with 9.3 units for 11 to 13-year-olds in 2009.

Compared with pupils in London schools, those in Yorkshire and the Humber had increased odds of having drunk alcohol in the last week. A comparative European study of drinking among 15–16-year-old European students showed 88% of British students had consumed alcohol during the past 12 months and more than half (57%) had been drunk during the same period. The estimated consumption on the latest drinking day (6.2 cl 100%) is well above ESPAD mean.

By the age of 15, pupils in the survey were more likely to have drunk alcohol (81%) than to have smoked (52%) or tried drugs (40%).

Binge-drinking patterns were more likely among drinkers from more deprived areas.

Survey findings can vary however. For example, the 2008 *TellUs3* survey showed significant differences to the above data in terms of the prevalence of young people who are drinking. This survey indicates that 25% of pupils aged ten to 15 said they had never had an alcoholic drink (compared to 46% of those in the sample from *Smoking, drinking and drug use among young people in England* in 2007.

It is important to note therefore that surveys offer a view on people's behaviour which may not always accurately reflect their actual behaviour.

January 2011

⇨ The above information is reprinted with kind permission from Alcohol Concern. Please visit www.alcoholconcern.org.uk for further information.

Local variations in youth drinking cultures

Does local area affect young people's drinking?

By Marion Roberts, Tim Townshend, Ilaria Pappalepore, Adam Eldridge and Budhi Mulyawan

This study explored the lives of young people in two regions of England where alcohol-related harm rates differ and found that:

⇨ the north has a higher degree of reported indicators of alcohol-related harms than the south-east and the south-west, but despite this young people's drinking behaviour in these areas followed similar patterns;

⇨ young people rarely drank on their own;

⇨ young people actively sought out clusters of youth-orientated bars, and sometimes these clusters encouraged young people to drink more than they intended;

⇨ planning authorities had often been unable to resist commercial pressures to allow clubs and bars to fill units that would otherwise be vacant, despite a wish to limit the number of licensed premises. This study explores the lives of young people, aged 15–24, in two study areas located in regions of England where the harm caused by alcohol is markedly different. The aim of the research was to explore whether living in these places influenced young people's drinking.

Key points

⇨ Significant differences in alcohol-related harms have been observed between English regions. The north has a higher degree of reported indicators of harms than the south-east and the south-west.

⇨ Despite these variations, young people's drinking behaviour in the two areas studied followed similar patterns with regard to their choice of drink, where they drank, and the days of the week and times at which they drank.

⇨ The differences between young people's behaviour in the case study areas was subtle and related to how those places had developed over long periods of time.

⇨ The primary motivation for drinking at all ages was sociability, having a good time and avoiding trouble. On a 'good night out', laughter and fun were important. In the case of the north-eastern city, this was a significant part of local culture. Young people rarely drank on their own.

⇨ Young people actively sought out 'clusters' of youth-orientated bars. A concentration of 'clusters' in the north east formed part of the impetus for young people to drink more than they originally intended.

⇨ In the south east, young people below the legal age of drinking engaged in a wider range of leisure activities, sports and hobbies.

⇨ In the north east, adult drinking was more visible both in the city centre and in streets and parks. There were more spaces where young people drank alongside adults.

Despite a wish to limit the number of licensed premises in the north east, planning authorities had been unable to resist commercial pressures to allow clubs and bars to fill units that would otherwise be vacant.

Background

Drinking is one of a variety of leisure activities that young people engage in. This study investigates drinking as an activity in terms of place, comparing an area in the south-east with low levels of alcohol-related harms and an area in the north-east with a higher level of harms.

The researchers examined how and where young people aged

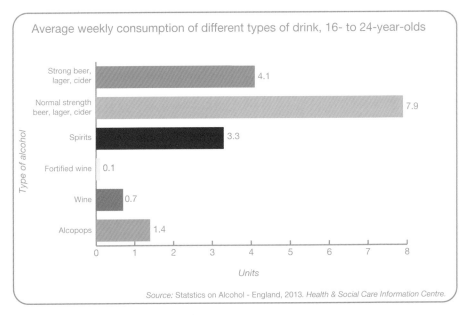

Average weekly consumption of different types of drink, 16- to 24-year-olds

Type of alcohol	Units
Strong beer, lager, cider	4.1
Normal strength beer, lager, cider	7.9
Spirits	3.3
Fortified wine	0.1
Wine	0.7
Alcopops	1.4

Source: Statstics on Alcohol - England, 2013. Health & Social Care Information Centre.

15–24 spent their leisure time. They asked them where they went, when, how often and who with. The study considered the impact of other leisure activities, the number and range of facilities, transport, policing and the influence of family or other role models.

Leisure activities

Young people in both case study areas shared many similar patterns of behaviour. At all ages, home was the place where they spent the most time, watching TV and DVDs, playing computer games, social networking, and listening to music. For teenagers below the legal age for drinking, favourite pastimes outside the home were spending time in local parks, going to shopping centres and going to the cinema.

The importance of sociability for drinking

Drinking was important to young people of all ages as a social activity. It was a rarity for a participant to report drinking alone. Teenagers below the legal age limit drank in parks and other open spaces and at home or friend's homes.

In the north-eastern area drinking outside was more commonplace, whereas in the south-eastern area teenage parties in people's homes were more significant. The study found little evidence of peer pressure in relation to under-18 drinking, though some peer selection was found.

In the north-eastern area, above the legal age for drinking, the balance shifted towards drinking in bars, clubs and pubs, although family barbecues and other celebrations were still important. In the south-eastern area, drinking at home continued to be important, although some participants felt constraints about drinking in front of their parents if they still lived at home. Home drinking was often associated with saving money.

The 'big night out'

The pattern of going out with a group of friends was common to both case study areas, with pre-drinking in groups at home or, more frequently in the north-eastern area, in a cheap bar or pub. Although some participants reported 'pre-drinking' to get drunk before going out, the majority reported its significance for reinforcing friendships. The 'night out' had elements of predictability and spontaneity. The pattern was to visit a number of bars, dance bars and nightclubs in succession, ending the night with fast food, a taxi or a lift home. The choice of bars and clubs to be visited was spontaneous and groups would form and re-form. There was no evidence of an established circuit and little evidence of peer pressure to continue drinking. Groups of friends looked out for each other and a good night out was one that involved some banter, listening or dancing to music and no problems (avoiding fights, being ill or being thrown out of venues). The most enthusiastic age for going on a night out was around 18, but participants with young families still reported the occasional 'big' night out.

Youth drinking venues

In both study areas young people actively chose to go to youth-oriented bars and clubs for a night out, and travelled up to 25 km, although 10 km was more widely reported. This was not due to any absence of 'traditional' pubs or other venues, which might be visited on other occasions. In the south-eastern area, young respondents were reluctant to visit venues with even slightly older (or younger) people on a night out.

Clusters and concentrations

The places visited on a night out had clusters of youth-oriented venues. Small towns with only one street of bars and clubs were as popular because they offered a different experience, such as the opportunity to dance or listen to music. The north-eastern area had one major city with a high concentration of youth-oriented venues separated into different clusters within the 1 km² area of the city centre. The close proximity of these licensed premises and the competition between them heightened the pressure to drink more. The atmosphere in the streets was more exuberant and uninhibited. This experience was diluted in the south-eastern area. There was less choice here and places where venues were located were further apart. Public transport was limited and did not function late into the night, whereas in the north-eastern area the public transport routes were focused on the city centre and ran relatively late. Driving was more common in the south-east and some participants reported that the need to drive after a heavy night out curbed their enthusiasm for going out. The need for a greater degree of organisation to arrange a night out acted as a constraint.

The importance of parks and other pastimes

For the younger age group, below the legal age of drinking, going out to clubs and pubs was not an option. This seems to have been a successful aspect of enforcement involving both the police and bar operators. The overwhelming majority of participants in the 15–16 age group commented that it was not worthwhile even to try to get into a pub or bar. The key difference between the leisure activities of this younger age group in the two case study areas was the variety of hobbies and pastimes outside the home enjoyed by the south-eastern participants. In addition to the mainstream activities of spending time in parks and shopping centres and going to the cinema, they reported hobbies such as going to drama groups, playing in bands, going to music lessons and volunteering, while in the north-east hobbies were more restricted, e.g. playing football or going to a local youth club. While some of the south-east activities, such as go-karting, were related to living in a more affluent household, other types of activity were linked to better services and facilities. In the south-eastern area, parks were more frequently praised for offering peaceful, restful spaces, whereas in the north-eastern area there were complaints about the parks being boring and having broken equipment. Dedicated facilities in the south-east, such as local authority and church youth clubs, were open at weekends and were in higher-quality buildings. There was also more evidence of support from the private sector in the south-east, for example with low concessionary rates in sports centres.

Visibility of heavy drinking

Under-18s were more likely to encounter adults drinking heavily in the north-eastern area. It was more commonplace to see street drinkers and young adults drinking in parks, streets and open spaces in local neighbourhoods. The most popular cinema for this age group in the city centre was located amongst a set of crowded bars and clubs, which started to attract customers from the late afternoon. The local planning authority had tried to diversify the city centre with more retail. In the case of one major development, they had to allow a change in use from retail to licensed premises to prevent units remaining vacant. This had also happened

with another development geared towards knowledge based enterprises.

Conclusions

The research team found that youth drinking behaviour was more about sociability than getting drunk. Youth drinking is seen as a 'problem' for regulation but the study recognises that there are positive attributes of drinking behaviours. The team found subtle variations between the two study areas. Place does have an influence over youth drinking behaviours, below and above the legal age limit. Many of the differences relate to urban layout, the qualities of particular spaces and the long-term impacts of licensing and planning policies. For young people, binge drinking is associated with parties and the 'big night out'. Age-segregated bars and clubs were particularly important and young people were prepared to travel considerable distances to go to them. The degree to which clusters of bars and clubs were dispersed across urban centres appeared to have an impact on the frequency and intensity of 'a good night out'. Licensing and planning authorities could encourage dispersal rather than concentration of youth drinking clusters to 'dilute' the experience. Encouraging the non-alcohol-related activities that are part of a night out, such as live music and dancing, could also reduce individual alcohol consumption. The extent to which excessive alcohol consumption is visible and hence 'normalised' was more apparent in the north-eastern study area. The team would recommend a greater distance between places where under-18s go, and bars and clubs. The study supports greater expenditure on, and more support for, leisure activities for under-18s. In the north-eastern sample, under-18s were more restricted by choice and access to non-alcohol-related youth leisure. Future planning in our towns and cities should ensure land is clearly allocated for such facilities and separated from alcohol-based leisure. The use

of vacant premises for temporary 'pop up' youth facilities should be investigated. The role of parks and shopping centres as the backdrop to young people's social lives needs more careful consideration. Young people spend a great deal of their leisure time in these 'public' spaces and must feel welcome and safe. This research suggests this is not necessarily the case.

About this project

The team used the same methods in both case study areas. Participants were drawn from similar backgrounds. Evidence was gathered from focus groups of 22–24-year-olds and 18–19-year-olds and semi-structured interviews. Young people aged 15–16 undertook a diary exercise followed by interviews alone or in small friendship groups.

28 August 2012

⇨ The above information is reprinted with kind permission from the Joseph Rowntree Foundation. Please visit www.jrf.org.uk for further information.

Skirting the issue: I drank alcohol aged 14 – and I turned out fine

Parents who give small amounts of alcohol to kids as young as 12 are not 'driving them to drink' – far from it, explains Louisa Peacock, whose father taught her how to be a responsible drinker.

This week a 'shocking' survey came out showing a quarter of parents have given their 12- to 14-year-olds a bit of drink while on holiday. I'm shocked the figure isn't higher, to be honest.

I mean, really, what's so shocking about it? It's not as though parents are encouraging their kids to get drunk: they're just allowing them to try – repeat 'try' – something which they see mum and dad do, and are probably intrigued about.

The parents concerned aren't luring their children into alcoholism from a young age, and they're certainly not encouraging under-age drinking. If anything, they will help their children to avoid the perils of seeking out booze aged 14 and drinking it on a park bench with their mates, totally unsupervised. We repeatedly hear about the problem this country has with women drinkers: could it be that because alcohol is such a total mystery for some girls growing up that when they're old enough to try it they go crazy?

Besides, young'uns trying a bit of drink from their parents' wine bottle will only discover that alcohol, at their age, tastes pretty rank and they won't feel the need to try it in a dirty alleyway or pub, away from their parents. They also won't have any peer pressure to pretend that they like it and carry on drinking it in said alleyway.

I realise the irony of me, as a non-parent, talking about this. You may say it gives me no right to comment. But I can speak as someone whose parents gave her a teeny-weeny bit of alcohol on the odd family special occasion, from when I was around 14, and the good that this has done me.

I remember my father specifically saying that he wanted us girls (me and my sister) to try a bit of alcohol now so that when we were older, and got to the pub, aged 18, we wouldn't go straight to the bar, down three pints in a row and become a complete idiot in front of all our mates, carrying on, well, like we'd never had a drink before. (No, those days came much later on, when I was old enough to know that would happen.)

It worked, too. I remember on my 18th birthday, I headed straight for a bar where I had a respectable few pints and went home practically sober. I didn't feel the need to 'get wasted' – I was sort of used to alcohol and its effects and knew better than to drink blindly until I lost control. (Again, those days were reserved for when I was at uni.)

You see, my dad saved me from the looming embarrassment of looking like a right plonker and being the laughing stock of my mates, having had too much booze at the age of 18. That, in my book, is good parenting. When I was older, and did indeed look like a right plonker in front of my friends thanks to one too many tequilas, that was of my own doing, my choice – it didn't catch me unawares as it would have done otherwise on my 18th birthday.

I can't say the same of my friends, who upon turning 18, headed straight to the nearest bar and got so drunk they ended up puking on the streets outside. Disgusting behaviour, I know – but can you really blame them? They had no clue what alcohol, or more to the point, alco-pops which taste like lemonade, would do to them. They'd never tried booze before and were so desperate to do so they didn't spare a second thought for the consequences of drinking too much. I don't know the exact time somebody coined the phrase 'binge drinking' but that night over ten years ago may have had something to do with it.

So next time someone is 'shocked' at the latest survey showing teenagers in Britain are trying alcohol under the safe supervision of their own parents, I hope they stop to think about the consequences of not doing so – which in reality could be far more shocking.

10 August 2013

⇨ The above information is reprinted with kind permission from *The Telegraph*. Please visit www.telegraph.co.uk for further information.

Breathing in the booze: calorie free alcohol in a diet obsessed society

Fancy smoking a beer? Is this new trend of inhaling alcohol a passing thing, or does it speak to real insecurities held by a lot of (overwhelmingly young) people?

Take a sniff to get smashed? It's quicker, cheaper, more effective, and apparently, hangover free! What's more, in an increasingly diet obsessed society, ditching swigging in favour of 'inhaling' has the added bonus of having a null calorie count. However, like all dieting fads, this latest drinking trend has inherent drawbacks and health risks which are potentially fatal.

Smoking shots and fizzing cocktails have become a standard feature in clubs across the world, and novelty and excess in alcohol consumption have seemingly inherent appeal in today's drinking culture. But recently a growing number of people have rejected the liquid component of a drunken night out altogether. Since a commercial device for converting liquid alcohol into vapour first appeared online in 2004, alcohol without liquid (AWOL) has increasingly ingratiated itself as a stronger, faster, and cooler way to enjoy a boozy night out. Videos demonstrating how to build and use a variety of homemade vaporising machines have appeared on the web, along with examples of how to employ dry ice and carbon dioxide pills to create alcoholic air. Footage of the 'awesome nights' which followed, accompanied by enthusiastic accounts of the speed, strength and style achieved through smoking booze are evidence of the increasing adoption of alcohol inhalation, particularly by America's youth.

In a society when speed is seemingly everything, going from sober to sloshed in a matter of minutes has an obvious appeal. Inhaling alcohol means it's absorbed straight into your brain and blood stream, getting you drunk very quickly. However, getting smashed by inhaling bypasses some of the body's in-built elimination mechanisms telling you when you've 'had enough'. The risk of alcohol poisoning or other drunken accidents through not knowing how much you're consuming is further exacerbated by the elimination of the body's natural recovery process. Breathing booze renders the traditional projectile vomiting, when you've hit the bottle too hard, less effective as a means of detoxifying your system, and there are fears that deaths from alcohol poisoning are likely to rise in line with the trajectory of AWOL's popularity.

Furthermore, it may be lacking in nicotine and tar, but that doesn't make smoking alcohol a healthy high. We are all well versed as to the negative impacts of smoking, and alcoholic vapour is also infused with harmful chemicals which can cause extensive damage to the lungs and brain. Despite many medical experts expressing concern over health risks, the relatively recent emergence of this drinking phenomenon means there is a lack of clinical evidence on the health risks and an ignorance or ambivalence in society. Furthermore, the element of danger and 'cool' associated with smoking alcohol potentially adds to its appeal, particularly attracting a rebellious and trend-chasing sector of the world's youth.

Drunkorexia

In addition to the dangers, and appeal, of smoking alcohol; the phenomenon could contribute to the already concerning existence of 'drunkorexia'. In an ever figure-focused society, an increasing number of people already sacrifice food in order to 'spend' calories on drinks. The option of a calorie free way to access alcohol is likely to hold a particularly strong attraction to those who are already struggling with this relatively unrecognised mental illness, increasing their vulnerability and risks to their health. The inherent dangers of AWOL are amplified to an even greater extent for those who are inhaling alcohol on an empty stomach and potentially already suffering from the negative physical health impacts of an eating disorder. However, with their priorities already perverted and skewed, drunkorexia sufferers are exactly the demographic of society most likely to find the option of inhaling alcohol an attractive alternative.

The dangers and health risks of alcohol – both through its physical effects and the social actions and attitudes it evokes – are already evident across the globe. Increasingly, alcohol consumption is becoming more and more extreme, both in quantity and how it is consumed. An increasing number of health risks are being identified, along with a range of social crises arising from a pervasive drinking culture. The rise of AWOL is particularly concerning through its intersecting of social insecurities, such as a desire to seem exciting or retain an 'ideal' body shape, with the exacerbation of health risks. An unhealthy and intensifying obsession with social pressures and expectations is intrinsically linked to society's relationship with alcohol, increasingly abused by the industry, cultivating dangerous drinking situations and methods.

These disturbing trends in drinking culture should herald a global recognition of the need to re-educate and re-evaluate society's relationship with alcohol. As a social lubricant and enjoyable treat, alcohol certainly has a long-established presence in our lives. However, there is a desperate need to develop an appreciation of the dangers of excessive or extreme alcohol consumption, and to promote positive alternatives for those who currently rely on alcohol to feel included and accepted.

*All views expressed in this article are the author's, and do not necessarily represent the views of 'It's the Drink Talking' or of Alcohol Concern.

19 June 2013

⇨ The above information is reprinted with kind permission from It's The Drink Talking. Please visit www.itsthedrinktalking.co.uk for further information.

Coca-Cola and Pepsi 'contain alcohol'

A recent study has revealed that more than half of leading cola soft drink brands contain small traces of alcohol.

Researchers from the National Institute of Consumption (INC) in Paris claim to have found low levels of alcohol (around 10 mg in every litre) in global Coca-Cola drinks, which is approximately 0.001% of alcohol per litre.

The brands tested positive for alcohol include Pepsi Cola, Coca-Cola Classic Light and Coke Zero.

In contrast, cheaper, supermarket brands of cola were alcohol-free.

The surprising results were published in the latest issue of the French magazine, *60 Million Consumers*.

'It is possible that traces of alcohol come from the process' of making Coca-Cola according to its secret recipe,' said Michel Pepin from Coca-Cola France, reports Channels TV.

Responding to the claims that these results will upset Muslim cola drinkers, Pepin added:

'Furthermore, the Paris Mosque has provided us with a certificate stating that our products can be consumed by the Muslim community in line with the religious opinions of the Committee of the Mosque of Paris.'

A spokesperson for Pepsi told *The Daily Mail* that they acknowledge 'soft drinks can contain minute traces of alcohol because of the ingredients used'.

Responding to the findings, Tamsin Kelly, editor of parenting website parentdish.co.uk, told *HuffPost Lifestyle*: 'I would think parents would be slightly appalled by news that so many colas contain traces of alcohol – all the more reason why these drinks should be a rare treat for children.'

29 June 2012

The above informtaion is reprinted with kind permission from *The Huffington Post UK*. Please visit www.huffingtonpost.co.uk for further information.

Guide to Freshers' Week nights out

New town, new friends – and you've got a week to get to know them before your lectures kick in. Your uni will have all kinds of nights laid on, and then there's the unplanned ones you'll just find yourself at! Keep any freshers' fatigue in check by reading our tips on how to do your first few nights at uni right.

Before heading out

Eating isn't cheating

Food helps slow the absorption of alcohol, stopping it going to your head too quickly so now's the time to put those student cooking skills to the test! Carbs or protein such as pasta, potatoes and chicken are good to eat before or while you're out drinking. They'll keep you full, and the slow release of energy will help you last the distance. You'll be more tempted to avoid that guilty 2am kebab or chips too.

Drinking before you go out?

If you drink too much, too early, you're much more likely to miss out on the proper night. There's nothing wrong in waiting until you're out to have your first alcoholic drink – mocktails are a great way to start the night. But if you and your new housemates have all got some pre-drinks in, alternate them with some water or soft drinks so you stay hydrated for the night ahead. Keep an eye on your home pouring too, especially when it comes to spirits. Pub/bar single shot measures are 25 ml, which doesn't look like a lot in a glass so don't be fooled into overpouring. Why not order one of our alcohol unit measure cups for your new digs?

Where do I live again?

It's easy to forget you're somewhere completely new. Plan your journey while you've got a clear head, and you've got a better chance of making it home without any surprise detours to the wrong part of town. If there's a last train, set a reminder on your phone so you don't get side tracked. Know where the buses stop and whether you need a ticket before you get on. Book a cab to save yourself a long wait; have a licensed cab number ready just in case or download the 'Good Times' app to book one from your location at the end of the night.

How did I spend that much?!

Ever had that sinking feeling in the morning, when you see the pile of receipts for drinks you don't remember buying? That's the last thing you want to wake up to when you know your student loan's got to last so why not leave your card at home and only take as much cash as you want to spend. Make sure you keep some in a separate pocket for getting yourself home safely too.

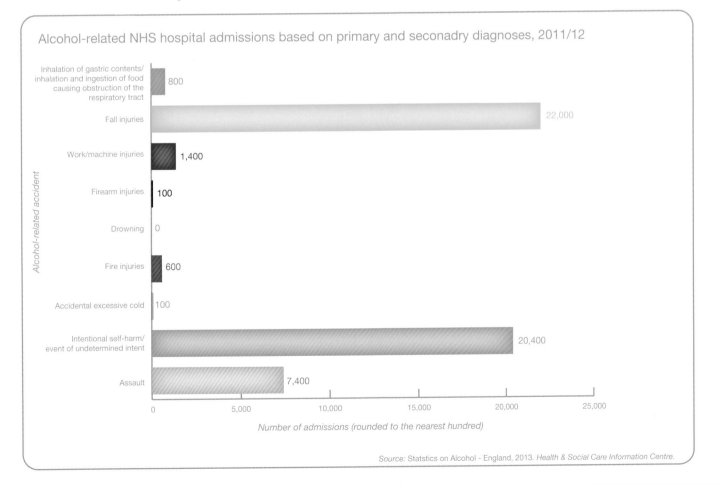

Alcohol-related NHS hospital admissions based on primary and seconadry diagnoses, 2011/12

Number of admissions (rounded to the nearest hundred)

Source: Statstics on Alcohol - England, 2013. *Health & Social Care Information Centre.*

While out

It's not a race, drink at your own pace

It takes up to an hour for your body to process each unit of alcohol. So have a break between drinks. Skinny, short, male, female… everyone copes with alcohol differently, so why try and keep up with your mates? Save face (and money) by sticking to smaller rounds with a couple of mates or avoid rounds altogether. Turning down a drink is much less embarrassing than throwing one up. Finish your drink too quickly and you'll feel pressured to get another. Instead, make your drink (and your night) last longer. Chat, sip, snack, drink water, get some fresh air and chat some more.

Looking good, my friend

For a great night, you want your new mates to be on top form too. So getting snacks and a jug of water for the table could be good for everyone. Look out for each other in case someone's getting ahead of themselves. If they are, grab them some water or a soft drink from the bar and encourage them to pace themselves – you don't want to have to put them in a cab, or worse, miss out on the night by having to take them home. If one of you does overdo it, make sure you know the difference between a bit too much and alcohol poisoning, and what to do if it's really serious.

Heading home

Mine's a pint... of water

If you stop drinking alcohol before the end of the evening and get some water in, your body can get a head start sorting itself out, which means getting home safely and less chance of a hangover tomorrow. Drink a glass of water when you get home too – you'll thank yourself in the morning!

Sticking together

Make sure you leave the pub or club in pairs or as a group. If someone's disappeared don't assume they've pulled, find out for sure! Don't leave anyone behind. It's not just the girls who need to watch out – lone blokes can attract trouble too. So keep a mate with you and try not to spend too much time hanging about at the end of the night.

Is your cab really a cab?

'Would you like a taxi?' Um. Depends if it really is one. Unlicensed cabbies are just blokes (usually) who go out late at night and find worse-for-wear people to drive home. As they're not regulated, you've got no way of knowing if the driver or vehicle is safe. No matter how late, there's no reason to go for a dodgy cab. Get some numbers for local cab firms stored on your phone or if you haven't done that the venue you're in will know of some. If you've got a long wait for a taxi, stay somewhere safe and well-lit until your cab turns up, ideally with a friend.

Download the Good Times app

You can download our free Good Times mobile app to:

⇨ Set up your night out as an event and invite your friends to it

⇨ Keep track of your mates on a map to make sure they're OK during and after the night

⇨ Find a taxi firm closest to your current location from the app's SOS section

⇨ Get great tips and advice straight to your phone throughout the night and the morning after.

And it's available for iPhone, Blackberry and Android!

September 2013

⇨ The above information is reprinted with kind permission from Drink Aware. Please visit www.drinkaware.co.uk for further information.

© Drink Aware 2013

Raising the price of alcohol, but at what cost?

By Josh Saunders

As you may or not be aware, the Government is considering increasing the price of alcohol to a minimum of 45p per unit in England, with Scotland proposing a price of 50p per unit. The Government and the Alcohol Health Alliance (AHA) take the stance this move will save taxpayers' money on alcohol-related hospital admissions and reduce booze-induced violent crime, whilst the drinks industry say it will hit 'safe-drinkers' the hardest without addressing the underlying problems. Let's face it, these are two sides of the argument presented by self-interest biased organisations. What is more interesting, however, is that barely anybody is talking about the impact this change in policy will have on the individual.

Alcohol abuse, at large, affects men more than women. According to Drinkaware.co.uk, the leading UK alcohol charity, men are more likely than women to binge drink and become alcohol dependent, and according to www.cdc.gov, men are more likely to drink prior to taking their own lives. It is widely acknowledged that alcohol dependency can be a cause, and a symptom, of depression, particularly in men. Alcohol consumption habits and excessive drinking in this country is an issue that needs to be addressed, but is raising the price of alcohol a panacea for irresponsible alcohol consumption and anti-social behaviour in the UK? Almost certainly not. It's fair to say that the tradition of 'going out on the piss' is so deeply entrenched in our society (Booze Britain, anyone?) that a price rise is the equivalent of putting an Elastoplast on a broken leg, but is it a step in the right direction?

Let's start by looking at the positives; after all, this isn't a notion that's appeared over-night. It's easy to see how the price increase could discourage people from binge-drinking. In today's economy, a lot of people are struggling to cover the basics, such as rent and food, let alone being able to afford regular sessions down the pub. The increase in the amount of pubs and venues that have closed down nationally over recent years is symptomatic of this reduction of readies in our wallets. A reduction in binge-drinking will inevitably lead to less alcohol-induced anti-social behaviour. In fact research, undertaken by Sheffield University for the Government in 2012, shows the price increase would reduce the amount of alcohol consumption by 4.3%, leading to 2,000 fewer alcohol-related deaths and 66,000 fewer hospital admissions after ten years. Researchers also suggested the number of crimes would drop by around 20,000 a year.

Some impressive figures there – 'suggested' rather than proven, of course – but attention grabbing, nonetheless. The aforementioned figures, however, relate to binge-drinking, but the CDC also states that 'most people who binge-drink are not alcoholics or alcohol dependent'. So what does this all mean for those who are dependent on alcohol?

Well, it's not going to force them all to stop, that's for sure. Alcoholic dependency is an addiction, a very serious one which, according to Alcohol Concern,

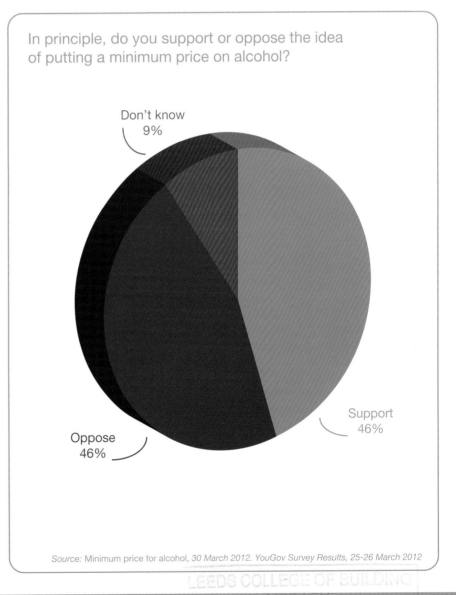

In principle, do you support or oppose the idea of putting a minimum price on alcohol?

Don't know
9%

Oppose
46%

Support
46%

Source: Minimum price for alcohol, 30 March 2012. YouGov Survey Results, 25-26 March 2012

currently affects 1.6 million people in the UK. It's also one of the only addictions that can result in death if the addict goes 'cold turkey' and, like any other dependency, alcoholics aren't necessarily able to quit drinking without external help.

'Alcohol abuse, at large, affects men more than women'

So, what does an alcoholic do in order to keep on drinking? In most cases, they will most likely spend even more of their money in order to fuel their addiction. And where does the money come from? Well, it could be from a number of places, some more extreme than others. Some may take out 'quick payday loans' at enormous interest rates and get into crippling debt, some may turn to crime, or maybe they'll spend less on their own, or worse, their children's, food...

'Alcohol dependency is an addiction, a very serious one which [...] currently affects 1.6 million people in the UK'

There's been a lot in the news over the last couple of years about the increase in sales of 'fake' or counterfeit alcohol since the recession hit in 2008, which is sold cheaply and can contain dangerous poisons and lethal amounts of methanol. According to a recent report from the Institute of Economic Affairs (IEA), counterfeit alcohol is costing the treasury £1.2 billion a year. This can have disastrous effects on physical and mental health. If the price of alcohol increases, it's safe to say that the amount of counterfeit alcohol sold will also increase. This isn't just going to affect people with alcohol dependencies. According to *The Sun*, back in late 2011 teens were setting up Facebook appreciation groups for the fake vodka brand Drops, for example Drops Vodka – memory loss in liquid form. There have already been a number of reported deaths from the consumption of fake alcohol. This is a problem that needs to be contained before it gets out of hand. Raising the price of legal alcohol will not help, according to the IEA: 'Evidence shows that the illicit alcohol market is closely associated with high taxes, corruption and poverty. The affordability of alcohol appears to be the key determinant behind the supply and demand for smuggled and counterfeit alcohol.' However, they continue: 'Demand for alcohol is relatively inelastic and drinkers have a series of options in front of them when real prices increase. They can do as the Government hopes and drink less, but they can also do any of the following: make savings elsewhere in the household budget, switch from the on-trade to the off-trade, downshift to cheaper drinks, shop abroad, brew or distil their own alcohol, buy counterfeit or smuggled alcohol, and, finally, buy surrogate alcohol (e.g. methanol, antifreeze, aftershave). The extent to which consumption patterns change depends on personal income and the price of drink.'

Sobering stuff

While the increase in the price of booze may reduce anti-social behaviour and binge-drinking to a point, it will not force alcoholics into giving up their addiction; it will simply make their addiction harder to maintain and with higher risks, and drive 'binge drinkers' towards cheaper and more dangerous highs. This could largely exacerbate the effects of depression in these people, and could have knock-on effects to people close to them. Alcoholics in general, especially the ones experiencing depression, don't need extra financial hardship and risk in their lives, they need a helping hand and it's safe to say that this new governmental price hike isn't the way to achieve that. This is not to suggest that booze should be cheap in order to allow alcoholics to continue drinking without risk, but should the plight of the addicted and the risk of counterfeit alcohol not be taken into consideration before this plan is put into action?

'Back in late 2011, teens were setting up Facebook appreciation groups for the fake vodka brand Drops... there have already been a number of reported deaths from the consumption of fake alcohol'

We're not saying scrap the plan, of course, we're just saying think of a plan that will have benefits and offer alternatives for individuals who need help, rather than just looking at the big figures. If a price rise is inevitable, perhaps some of the extra revenue raised could be invested in more comprehensive and readily available alcohol dependency treatment centres or community advisory services? We understand the potential benefits. The fact is that some people turn to alcohol as a result of depression, and some people become depressed as a result of alcohol abuse. This plan has the possibility to prevent people from getting into heavy drinking in the first place which is a good thing for those not already in the grips of addiction. However, for the policy to really benefit everyone, more needs to be done to help the people that already have real alcohol problems and raising the price of alcohol is not the answer.

15 January 2013

⇨ The above information is reprinted with kind permission from CALM. Please visit www.thecalmzone.net for further information.

The beer story: facts on tap

The truth behind taxes, jobs and the future of the industry.

Why do beer and pubs matter?

UK plc

Beer is a major British product and a major tax contributor. There are now over 1,000 breweries in the UK.

Beer and pubs contribute £19 billion to UK GDP and generate £10 billion in tax revenue.

Jobs

The production and sale of beer creates jobs in agriculture, brewing, pubs and the wider supply chain.

In total the beer and pub sector support one million UK jobs. 46% of those employed in the sector are 16–24-year-olds.

Responsible drinking

The beer and pub sector is working with the Government to reduce alcohol abuse.

Harmful drinking has nearly halved in the last decade to 4% of the population. Alcohol consumption has fallen by 13% since 2004.

Pubs at the heart of the community

Beer supports pubs

At the heart of every pub is beer, mostly British-brewed, often locally. Beer is enjoyed by almost 32 million adults.

Bringing people together

Pubs are places where people socialise, relax and make connections. It's the original social network. The pub is the focal point of any community, playing a unique role in national life.

Vibrant small businesses

Pubs inject an average of £80,000 into their local economy and pay £66,500 in beer tax every year. Nearly 90% of

pubs are community or rural pubs, bringing much-needed employment to areas of the UK – these small businesses are vital to the economy.

Providing community services

Many pubs provide a range of important public services, including post offices, local shops and broadband internet access. They also hold a variety of community events and activities, such as live music, that add to local culture.

Promoting responsible drinking

Pubs are supervised environments and take responsible drinking seriously. The industry invests millions in Drinkaware, Best Bar None, Pubwatch and Challenge 21.

Bitter tax facts

Beer duty escalator: over the top

In 2008 the Government made a commitment to above-inflation duty increases on beer. This is known as the beer duty escalator and is in place until 2014/15. As a result of the escalator, the average pub pint now costs £3.10.

Beer duty escalator: going nowhere

Beer duty is now so high that demand has gone down. Pubs sell a billion fewer pints per year since the introduction of the escalator. With the escalator set to rise again in 2013/14, the net effect could result in a £2 million loss to the Treasury.

UK has higher beer duty than all its EU neighbours

Massive differences in duty contribute to fraud, which damages the UK economy. Britons pay 40% of the EU beer tax bill, but only consume 13% of the beer sold in Europe.

What should the Government do?

1. Freeze beer duty

It's time to recognise the economic and social value of the Great British beer and pub industry. A pint in a pub should not be an unaffordable luxury.

2. Scrap the escalator

Beer tax has risen by 42% since its introduction in March 2008, making further rises unsustainable. Total beer tax revenues are now flat, as beer sales have dropped and consumer incomes have fallen.

3. Rebalance alcohol taxation

The Government should use the tax system to encourage consumers towards lower-strength, British-made drinks.

⇨ The above information is reprinted with kind permission from the British Beer & Pub Association. Please visit www.beerandpub.com for further information.

Key facts

⇨ Drinking too much over a short period of time can cause liver disease and increases the risk of some kinds of cancer. (page 1)

⇨ One unit is equal to 10 ml of alcohol. (page 2)

⇨ The safe weekly limit for women is 14 units of alcohol, and for men is 21 units. (page 2)

⇨ In any one day, it is best for a man to drink no more than four units and for a woman to drink no more than three units. Drinking over eight units a day for men, or six units a day for women is known as 'binge drinking'. (page 2)

⇨ All alcohol sold in the UK that is above 1.2% ABV (Alcohol By Volume) should state how strong it is in percentages (%). (page 2)

⇨ A pint of lager is 5% ABV, contains 233 calories and 2.8 units of alcohol. A spirit shot, by contrast, is 40% ABV and contains 61 calories and 1 unit of alcohol. (page 5)

⇨ Around nine in 100 men and four in 100 women show signs of being dependent on alcohol. (page 8)

⇨ More than 178,000 prescriptions to treat alcohol dependency were issued in 2012. (page 10)

⇨ The net cost of ingredients in prescriptions for alcohol dependency in 2012 was £2.93 million. (page 10)

⇨ A 174 ml glass of red wine is equivalent to two units of alcohol. (page 12)

⇨ If you drink three glasses of 250ml wine, you're drinking a whole bottle, which is three times the recommended amount. (page 12)

⇨ A pint of beer contains 2.3 units of alcohol. (page 12)

⇨ A survey found that around three in ten adults drink more than the recommended amount of alcohol on at least one day each week. (page 12)

⇨ Since 2005, HMRC has seized nearly 15 million litres of illegally produced alcohol. (page 13)

⇨ An estimated 1.22 million hospital admissions in England were linked to drinking too much alcohol in 2011–2012. (page 14)

⇨ Hospital admissions for which drink was the main cause rose to 200,900 in 2011–2012, more than 40% up on 2002–2003. (page 14)

⇨ In Canada, a 10% increase in minimum unit price caused a 32% reduction in deaths. (page 14)

⇨ Nearly 50 per cent of all violent crime is alcohol related. (page 15)

⇨ If you drink and drive, alcohol can reduce your ability to see distant objects and night vision can be reduced by up to 25%. (page 16)

⇨ Traffic accidents are still a leading cause of alcohol-related deaths among young men aged 16- to 24-years-old. (page 16)

⇨ In the UK the alcohol limit for drivers is 80 mg of alcohol per 100 ml of blood, 35 mg per 100 ml of breath per 107 mg per 100 ml of urine. (page 16)

⇨ Of the 4,000 fatal accidents that happen in homes in the UK every year, 400 are alcohol-related. (page 16)

⇨ Muslim countries and eight out of the 27 EU member states do not have readily accessible alcohol consumption guidelines. (page 18)

⇨ 69% of people surveyed by YouGov and *The Sunday Times*, believe that they would be healthier if they had two alcohol-free days each week. (page 20)

⇨ Self-reported alcohol consumption only accounts for between 40 and 60% of sales. (page 23)

Alcohol

The type of alcohol found in drinks, ethanol, is an organic compound. The ethanol in alcoholic beverages such as wine and beer is produced through the fermentation of plants containing carbohydrates. Ethanol can cause intoxication if drunk excessively.

Alcohol By Volume (ABV)

ABV is a measure of how much pure alcohol is present in a drink. It is represented as a percentage of the total volume of the drink. For example, a one-litre bottle of an alcoholic beverage will provide an ABV value on its label. This informs the buyer what percentage of that one litre consists of pure alcohol.

Alcohol dependency/alcoholism

Alcohol is a drug and it is addictive. If someone becomes dependent on drink to the extent that they feel they need it just to get through the day, they may be referred to as an alcoholic. In addition to the various health problems related to alcoholism, an alcoholic's relationships and career may also suffer due to their addiction. They can suffer withdrawal symptoms if they don't drink alcohol regularly and may need professional help from an organisation such as Alcoholics Anonymous to deal with their dependency.

Binge drinking

When an individual consumes large quantities of alcohol in one session, usually with the intention of becoming drunk, this is popularly referred to as 'binge drinking'. It is widely accepted that drinking four or more drinks in a short space of time constitutes 'bingeing', and this can have severe negative effects on people's health.

Depressant

A drug that temporarily causes a decrease or 'slowing down' of the body's mental and/or physical functions.

Drink spiking

When someone adds alcohol or drugs to another person's drink without their knowledge or consent, it is said that their drink has been 'spiked'. Drink spiking is sometimes, but not always, done in order to facilitate another crime such as rape or assault. Prevention strategies include using a 'stopper' in the tops of bottles to prevent anything being added to the drink, and never leaving a drink alone.

Hangover

A hangover describes the effects of alcohol the day after intoxication. Alcohol is a depressant, causes the body to dehydrate and also irritates the stomach, so hangovers usually involve a severe headache, nausea, diarrhoea, a depressive mood and tiredness. There are many myths about how to cure a hangover but the only real solution is to drink plenty of water and wait for it to pass – or of course to drink less alcohol in the first place!

Intoxication

The state of being drunk, caused by drinking too much alcohol. Drunkenness can lead to dizziness, sickness, loss of memory, aggression or anti-social behaviour, as well as potentially causing long-term health problems such as cirrhosis of the liver. Due to the loss of inhibitions associated with heavy alcohol use, it can also cause people to indulge in risk-taking behaviour they would not normally consider – for example, having unprotected sex.

Teetotal

A teetotaller is someone who abstains completely from alcohol. If an individual is trying to recover from an alcohol dependency they will usually be teetotal. However, people do not drink for many other reasons, including religion, pregnancy, for health reasons or just through personal preference.

Unit

The unit system is a method used to measure the strength of an alcoholic drink. One unit is 10ml of pure alcohol – the amount of alcohol the average adult can process within the space of one hour. Units can be calculated by multiplying the amount of alcohol in millilitres by the drink's ABV, and dividing by 1,000.

Assignments

Brainstorming

⇨ In small groups, brainstorm to find out what you know about alcohol. You should consider the following questions:

- What is alcohol?

- What are the effects of drinking alcohol? Both long- and short-term.

- What is alcohol dependency?

Research

⇨ Search the Internet to find some newspaper headlines about fake alcohol. Make some notes, or print out some examples, and share with your class.

⇨ Find out what would happen if you were caught driving with too much alcohol in your system? What is the maximum penalty you could receive?

⇨ Read the article *Is it time for global alcohol consumption guidelines.* Choose a country outside of Europe and investigate their alcohol consumption guidelines. Make some notes that detail your findings and feedback to your class.

⇨ Research the facilities available in your local area for those who think they might have a problem with alcohol dependency. Create a flyer that details these facilities.

⇨ Talk to your parents, friends or relatives who have lived in your local area for a long time. Ask them about the pubs that used to be open in the area and find out how many have recently closed-down. What is the effect on the local community when a pub closes? Write a summary of your findings, no longer than one sheet of A4.

Design

⇨ Read the article *Long-term effects* on page 5. Create a poster that illustrates the possible long-term effects of drinking alcohol.

⇨ In pairs or small groups, design a series of adverts that will feature on the Internet and in magazines to draw attention to the negative short-term effects of drinking alcohol.

⇨ Design a leaflet that will provide young people with key facts about alcohol.

⇨ Design a non-alcoholic drinks brand that could compete with alcopops like Bacardi Breezer and Smirnoff Ice to be a popular drink among students and young people who don't want to drink alcohol. You should think of a name, a flavour and a bottle/label design. Work in pairs or individually.

⇨ Design an app that will allow people to quickly and easily check how many units of alcohol are in their drinks.

Oral

⇨ In pairs, discuss whether you think the 'drunk tank' scheme is a good idea. See the article on page 15 for further information.

⇨ Stage a class debate in which half of the class argues that the legal drinking age should be increased to 21 and half argue that it should remain the same.

⇨ In pairs, role-play a situation in which one of you is about to go to university and is concerned about Freshers' Week because you don't like drinking alcohol. You should take it in turns to play the part of the friend giving advice and the student going to university.

⇨ Imagine that you work at a local pub which is in danger of having to close. You need more customers but want to promote responsible drinking. What could you do? Discuss in pairs.

⇨ Look at the graph on page 11. Over the last decade, alcohol consumption in the home has remained steady, whereas alcohol consumption out of the home has declined. Why do you think this is? Discuss in small groups.

Reading/writing

⇨ Write an article for your local newspaper, exploring the dangers of fake alcohol.

⇨ Read Louisa Peacock's article on page 32. Do you agree that parents can teach their children to be responsible drinkers by encouraging them to try alcohol before the age of 18? Write a blog post exploring your response to Louisa's article.

⇨ Do you think the minimum price of alcohol should be increased? Write a letter to your local MP explaining your opinion.

⇨ 'Drinking alcohol is as dangerous as taking drugs.' Write a two-page essay exploring whether you agree or disagree with this statement.

Acknowledgements

The publisher is grateful for permission to reproduce the material in this book. While every care has been taken to trace and acknowledge copyright, the publisher tenders its apology for any accidental infringement or where copyright has proved untraceable. The publisher would be pleased to come to a suitable arrangement in any such case with the rightful owner.

Images

Cover, pages iii and 3: iStock, page 4: iStock, page 10: iStock, page 14: iStock, page 17: MorgueFile, page 18: iStock, page 19 © Jackie Staines, page 23 © Jackie Staines, page 27: iStock, page 39 © Jackie Staines.

Illustrations

Page 6: Don Hatcher, page 15: Simon Kneebone, page 26: Angelo Madrid, page 28: Simon Kneebone, page 33: Angelo Madrid, page 36: Don Hatcher.

Additional acknowledgements

Editorial on behalf of Independence Educational Publishers by Cara Acred.

With thanks to the Independence team: Mary Chapman, Sandra Dennis, Christina Hughes, Jackie Staines and Jan Sunderland.

Cara Acred

Cambridge, January 2014